WHERE AM I NOW?

DATE
_____

WEIGHT
_____

HEIGHT
_____

BODY FAT %
_____

_____

_____

BEFORE PHOTO

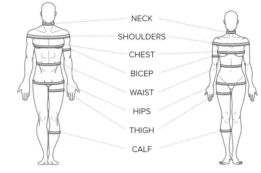

NECK

SHOULDERS

CHEST

BICEP

WAIST

HIPS

THIGH

CALF

MEASUREMENTS (CIRCUMFERENCE)

NECK
_____

SHOULDERS
_____

CHEST
_____

BICEP (FLEXED)
_____

WAIST
_____

HIPS
_____

THIGH
_____

CALF
_____

_____

GOALS

WEIGHT
_____

BODY FAT %
_____

NECK
_____

SHOULDERS
_____

CHEST
_____

BICEP (FLEXED)
_____

WAIST
_____

HIPS
_____

THIGH
_____

CALF
_____

_____

HOW TO PERFORM SKIN-FOLD BODY FAT % MEASUREMENT

These instructions will help you perform the easiest, most consistent "three-site Jackson and Pollock" skin-fold test. You will need to purchase an inexpensive body fat caliper to proceed. The basic idea of a skin-fold test is to "pinch and pull." Separate the fat tissue from the surrounding tissue with a good pinch, and then pull away from the body just slightly. Place the calipers about 1 cm to the side of your fingers and take your reading.

❶ SKIN-FOLD MEASUREMENT

❷ SKIN-FOLD MEASUREMENT

❸ SKIN-FOLD MEASUREMENT

Visit **bodyfat.newmefitness.net**, enter your measurements, and the form will calculate your body fat percentage.

BODYFAT %

MALE

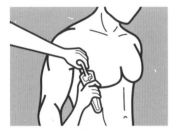

❶ **Chest:** Diagonal fold, midway between upper armpit and nipple

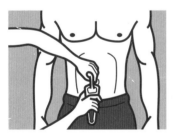

❷ **Abdominal:**
Vertical fold, one inch to the right of navel

❸ **Thigh:** Vertical fold, midway between kneecap and top of thigh

FEMALE

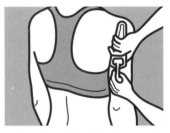

❶ **Triceps:** Vertical fold, midway between elbow and shoulder

❷ **Suprailiac:** Diagonal fold, directly above iliac crest or hip bone

❸ **Thigh:** Vertical fold, midway between kneecap and top of thigh

DETERMINING YOUR IDEAL DAILY CALORIE INTAKE

The number of calories you need each day depends on a number of factors, including your age, gender, height, weight, and level of activity. Our calculator can help you determine your ideal daily calorie intake if you want to maintain your current weight. And if your goal is to lose weight, you'll need to consume fewer calories than you expend, and vice versa if you want to gain weight.

Visit **bmr.newmefitness.net**, enter your information, and the form will calculate your daily calorie needs, as well as the following:

LBM (lean body mass—total body weight, not counting any weight from fat)
BMR (basal metabolic rate—the number of calories burned each day without exercise)
TDEE (total daily energy expenditure—the number of calories burned each day, including those burned through exercise)

My LBM: _____

My BMR: _____

My TDEE: _____

My goal: ☐ Lose weight   ☐ Maintain weight   ☐ Gain weight

My ideal daily calorie intake: _____

IDEAL BODY FAT PERCENTAGE CHART (American Council On Exercise)		
Description	**Men**	**Women**
Essential Fat	2–5%	10–13%
Athletes	6–13%	14–20%
Fitness	14–17%	21–24%
Average	18–24%	25–31%
Obese	25%+	32%+

TRACK YOUR PROGRESS

WEIGHT ▶▶▶▶▶▶

WEEK 1	WEEK 2	WEEK 3	WEEK 4	WEEK 5	WEEK 6	WEEK 7	WEEK 8	WEEK 9	WEEK 10

WEEK 11	WEEK 12	WEEK 13	WEEK 14	WEEK 15	WEEK 16	WEEK 17	WEEK 18	WEEK 19	WEEK 20

BODY FAT % ▶▶▶▶▶▶

WEEK 1	WEEK 2	WEEK 3	WEEK 4	WEEK 5	WEEK 6	WEEK 7	WEEK 8	WEEK 9	WEEK 10

WEEK 11	WEEK 12	WEEK 13	WEEK 14	WEEK 15	WEEK 16	WEEK 17	WEEK 18	WEEK 19	WEEK 20

WAIST SIZE:

WEEK 1	WEEK 2	WEEK 3	WEEK 4	WEEK 5	WEEK 6	WEEK 7	WEEK 8	WEEK 9	WEEK 10

WEEK 11	WEEK 12	WEEK 13	WEEK 14	WEEK 15	WEEK 16	WEEK 17	WEEK 18	WEEK 19	WEEK 20

ITEM TO TRACK:

WEEK 1	WEEK 2	WEEK 3	WEEK 4	WEEK 5	WEEK 6	WEEK 7	WEEK 8	WEEK 9	WEEK 10

WEEK 11	WEEK 12	WEEK 13	WEEK 14	WEEK 15	WEEK 16	WEEK 17	WEEK 18	WEEK 19	WEEK 20

ITEM TO TRACK:

WEEK 1	WEEK 2	WEEK 3	WEEK 4	WEEK 5	WEEK 6	WEEK 7	WEEK 8	WEEK 9	WEEK 10

WEEK 11	WEEK 12	WEEK 13	WEEK 14	WEEK 15	WEEK 16	WEEK 17	WEEK 18	WEEK 19	WEEK 20

ITEM TO TRACK:

WEEK 1	WEEK 2	WEEK 3	WEEK 4	WEEK 5	WEEK 6	WEEK 7	WEEK 8	WEEK 9	WEEK 10

WEEK 11	WEEK 12	WEEK 13	WEEK 14	WEEK 15	WEEK 16	WEEK 17	WEEK 18	WEEK 19	WEEK 20

ITEM TO TRACK:

WEEK 1	WEEK 2	WEEK 3	WEEK 4	WEEK 5	WEEK 6	WEEK 7	WEEK 8	WEEK 9	WEEK 10

WEEK 11	WEEK 12	WEEK 13	WEEK 14	WEEK 15	WEEK 16	WEEK 17	WEEK 18	WEEK 19	WEEK 20

RESULTS

DATE

WEIGHT

HEIGHT

BODY FAT %

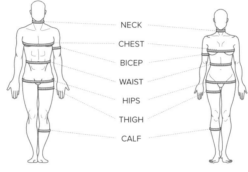

NECK

CHEST

BICEP

WAIST

HIPS

THIGH

CALF

MEASUREMENTS
(CIRCUMFERENCE)

NECK

CHEST

BICEP (FLEXED)

WAIST

HIPS

THIGH

CALF

CALORIES & MACROS FOR COMMON FOODS

The following chart lists many common foods with their calories and macro information. For information on foods not listed here, visit **nutritiondata.self.com** or **nutritionix.com**.

MEAT, FISH & PROTEIN

FOOD	Serving	Protein (g)	Fat (g)	Carbs (g)	Calories (g)
Chicken breast, boneless skinless	1 half breast (118 g)	27.2	1.5	0	130
Chicken thigh, boneless skinless	1 thigh (52 g)	13.5	5.7	0	109
Ground beef (75% lean)	100 g (1/2 cup)	15.8	25	0	293
Salmon	100 g	19.8	6.3	0	142
Tuna (albacore, canned in water)	100 g	25.5	.8	0	116
Shrimp	100 g (10 medium)	20.3	1.7	.9	106
Ham	113 g (4 oz)	31.4	9.4	.3	220
Bacon	16 g (about 2 cooked strips)	3	3.1	.1	41.3
Tofu, firm	¼ block (81 g)	12.8	7.4	3.5	117

DAIRY & EGGS

FOOD	Serving	Protein (g)	Fat (g)	Carbs (g)	Calories (g)
Milk, full-fat (whole)	8 oz (1 cup)	8	7.9	12	149
Milk, low-fat (2%)	8 oz (1 cup)	8	4.8	12	122
Milk, skim (nonfat)	8 oz (1 cup)	8	.2	12	83
Yogurt, plain low-fat	8 oz (1 cup)	12.9	3.8	17.2	154
Yogurt, plain nonfat	8 oz (1 cup)	14	.4	18.8	137
Cottage cheese, low-fat	1 oz	7	.7	1	24
Cheddar cheese	1 oz	7	9.4	.4	114
Parmesan cheese	1 oz	10	7.3	.9	111
Mozzarella cheese	1 oz	6.3	6.3	.6	85
Butter, unsalted	1 tbsp (14 g)	.1	11.4	0	100
Eggs	1 large (50 g)	6.3	5	0	71.5
Almondmilk, unsweetened	8 oz (1 cup)	1	2.5	1	30
Soy milk, unsweetened	8 oz (1 cup)	7	4	3	80

GRAINS

FOOD	Serving	Protein (g)	Fat (g)	Carbs (g)	Calories (g)
Oats	1 cup cooked	5.9	3.6	28.1	166
White rice	1 cup cooked	4.3	.4	45	205
Brown rice	1 cup cooked	5.5	2	52	216
Quinoa	1 cup cooked	8.1	3.6	39.4	222
Pasta (elbow macaroni)	1 cup cooked	8.1	1.3	43.2	221
Whole-wheat bread	1 slice (26 g)	3.5	1.1	11.3	68.9
White bread	1 slice (26 g)	1.9	.8	12.7	66.5

NUTS, BEANS & LEGUMES

FOOD	Serving	Protein (g)	Fat (g)	Carbs (g)	Calories (g)
Walnuts	1 oz (28 g), about 14 walnut halves	4.3	18.3	3.8	183
Pecans	1 ounce (28 g), about 15 pecan halves	2.6	20.2	3.9	193
Almonds	1 ounce (28 g), about 23 almonds	13.8	6.1	161	5.9
Peanuts	1 ounce (28 g), about 35 peanuts	7.3	13.9	4.4	160
Peanut butter, smooth	2 tbsp (32 g)	8	16.1	6.4	188
Chickpeas (garbanzo beans)	1 cup cooked (220 g)	11.9	2.7	54.3	286
Black beans	1 cup cooked (172 g)	15	.9	40	225
Red kidney beans	1 cup cooked (223 g)	15	.9	40	223
Lentils	1 cup cooked (198 g)	17.9	.8	39.9	230

FRUITS & VEGETABLES

FOOD	Serving	Protein (g)	Fat (g)	Carbs (g)	Calories (g)
Apples	1 medium (182 g)	.5	.3	25	95
Oranges	1 small (96 g)	.9	.1	11.3	45
Peaches	1 medium (150 g)	1.4	.4	14.8	59
Blueberries	1 cup (148 g)	1.1	.5	21.4	84
Strawberries	1 cup whole berries (144 g)	1	.4	11	46
Bananas	1 medium (118 g)	1.3	.4	27	105
Grapes	1 cup whole grapes (151 g)	1.1	.2	27.3	104
Watermelon	1 wedge (286 g)	1.7	.4	21	85
Avocados	1 medium	2.7	21	11.8	227
Tomatoes	1 medium	1.1	.2	4.8	22
Corn	1 medium ear (90 g)	2.9	1.1	17.1	77
Carrots	1 medium (61 g)	.6	.1	5.8	25
Green peppers	1 medium (119 g)	1.0	.2	5.5	24
Lettuce (romaine)	1 large leaf (28 g)	.3	.1	.9	5
Potatoes (white)	1 medium (213 g)	4.3	.2	39.2	164
Potatoes (sweet)	1 small (130 g)	2.0	.1	26.2	112
Onions (white)	1 cup, chopped (130 g)	1.8	.2	14.9	64
Broccoli	1 cup chopped (91 g)	2.6	.3	6	31

An optimal diet is a mix of carbohydrates, protein, and fat.
Each of these has a different calorie count:
1 gram of carbohydrates = 4 calories
1 gram of fat = 9 calories
1 gram of protein = 4 calories

If you're striving to boost your metabolism and/or build muscle, aim for this ratio:
40 percent protein, 35 percent carbohydrates, 25 percent fat

If you want to lose fat, your diet should look like this:
45 percent protein, 35 percent carbohydrates, 20 percent fat

Note that various diets, such as Keto or Slow Carb, call for different macro ratios. Our logbook is flexible and works equally well if you're following one of these diets.

DATE | | | □□□□□□ **WEIGHT** | **SLEEP** | **WATER**
S M T W T F S | POUNDS/KILOS | HOURS | OZ/ml

HOW I FEEL 😄 😊 😐 😟 **ENERGY** 🔋⊏⊐⊐⊐⊐⊐🔋 **ACTIVITY** 🛏⊏⊐⊐⊐⊐🏃

☐ SUGAR FREE ☐ ALCOHOL FREE ☐ GLUTEN FREE ☐ DAIRY FREE ☐ LOW CARB ☐ LOTS OF VEGGIES
☐ ORGANIC ☐ NO PROCESSED FOODS

BREAKFAST TIME:	SERVING SIZE	PROTEIN	FAT	CARBS	CALORIES
SUBTOTAL					
LUNCH TIME:					
SUBTOTAL					
DINNER TIME:					
SUBTOTAL					
SNACKS TIME: / / /					
TOTAL					
vs. TARGET					

NOTES
_____
_____
_____
_____

HOW THE DAY WENT? ☐ BAD ☐ OK ☐ GOOD ☐ GREAT

DATE | | | ☐☐☐☐☐☐☐ **WEIGHT** **SLEEP** **WATER**
S M T W T F S   POUNDS/KILOS   HOURS   OZ/ml

HOW I FEEL 😀 🙂 😐 🙁   **ENERGY** ▢ ⊂━━━━⊃ 🔋   **ACTIVITY** 🛏 ⊂━━━━⊃ 🏃

☐ SUGAR FREE   ☐ ALCOHOL FREE   ☐ GLUTEN FREE   ☐ DAIRY FREE   ☐ LOW CARB   ☐ LOTS OF VEGGIES
☐ ORGANIC   ☐ NO PROCESSED FOODS

BREAKFAST TIME:	SERVING SIZE	PROTEIN	FAT	CARBS	CALORIES
SUBTOTAL					
LUNCH TIME:					
SUBTOTAL					
DINNER TIME:					
SUBTOTAL					
SNACKS TIME: / / /					
TOTAL					
vs. TARGET					

NOTES
_____
_____
_____
_____

HOW THE DAY WENT? ☐ BAD ☐ OK ☐ GOOD ☐ GREAT

DATE | | S M T W T F S | **WEIGHT** | **SLEEP** | **WATER**
| | POUNDS/KILOS | HOURS | OZ/ml

HOW I FEEL 😄 🙂 😐 ☹️   ENERGY 🔋 ▭▭▭▭▭ 🔋   ACTIVITY 🛏️ ▭▭▭▭▭ 🏃

☐ SUGAR FREE ☐ ALCOHOL FREE ☐ GLUTEN FREE ☐ DAIRY FREE ☐ LOW CARB ☐ LOTS OF VEGGIES
☐ ORGANIC ☐ NO PROCESSED FOODS

BREAKFAST TIME:	SERVING SIZE	PROTEIN	FAT	CARBS	CALORIES
SUBTOTAL					

LUNCH TIME:					
SUBTOTAL					

DINNER TIME:					
SUBTOTAL					

SNACKS TIME: / / /					
TOTAL					
vs. TARGET					

NOTES
_____
_____
_____
_____

HOW THE DAY WENT? ☐ BAD ☐ OK ☐ GOOD ☐ GREAT

DATE | |

S M T W T F S

WEIGHT
POUNDS/KILOS

SLEEP
HOURS

WATER
OZ/ml

HOW I FEEL ☺ ☺ ☹ ☹   ENERGY 🔋⊂▭▭▭▭⊃🔋   ACTIVITY 🛌⊂▭▭▭▭⊃🏃

☐ SUGAR FREE   ☐ ALCOHOL FREE   ☐ GLUTEN FREE   ☐ DAIRY FREE   ☐ LOW CARB   ☐ LOTS OF VEGGIES
☐ ORGANIC   ☐ NO PROCESSED FOODS

BREAKFAST TIME:	SERVING SIZE	PROTEIN	FAT	CARBS	CALORIES
SUBTOTAL					

LUNCH TIME:					
SUBTOTAL					

DINNER TIME:					
SUBTOTAL					

SNACKS TIME: / / /					
TOTAL					
vs. TARGET					

NOTES
_____
_____
_____
_____

HOW THE DAY WENT? ☐ BAD ☐ OK ☐ GOOD ☐ GREAT

DATE _____ | _____ | _____

☐☐☐☐☐☐☐
S M T W T F S

WEIGHT
_____
POUNDS/KILOS

SLEEP
_____
HOURS

WATER
_____
OZ/ml

HOW I FEEL 😃 🙂 😐 ☹️   **ENERGY** 🔋 ⊏▭▭▭▭⊐ 🔋   **ACTIVITY** 🛏️ ⊏▭▭▭⊐ 🏃

☐ SUGAR FREE ☐ ALCOHOL FREE ☐ GLUTEN FREE ☐ DAIRY FREE ☐ LOW CARB ☐ LOTS OF VEGGIES
☐ ORGANIC ☐ NO PROCESSED FOODS

BREAKFAST TIME:	SERVING SIZE	PROTEIN	FAT	CARBS	CALORIES
SUBTOTAL					
LUNCH TIME:					
SUBTOTAL					
DINNER TIME:					
SUBTOTAL					
SNACKS TIME: / / /					
TOTAL					
vs. TARGET					

NOTES
_____
_____
_____
_____

HOW THE DAY WENT? ☐ BAD ☐ OK ☐ GOOD ☐ GREAT

DATE | | | S M T W T F S | **WEIGHT** | **SLEEP** | **WATER**
| | POUNDS/KILOS | HOURS | OZ/ml

HOW I FEEL ☺ ☺ ☺ ☹   **ENERGY** 🔋⊂▭▭▭⊃🔋   **ACTIVITY** 🛏⊂▭▭▭⊃🏃

☐ SUGAR FREE ☐ ALCOHOL FREE ☐ GLUTEN FREE ☐ DAIRY FREE ☐ LOW CARB ☐ LOTS OF VEGGIES
☐ ORGANIC ☐ NO PROCESSED FOODS

BREAKFAST TIME:	SERVING SIZE	PROTEIN	FAT	CARBS	CALORIES
SUBTOTAL					
LUNCH TIME:					
SUBTOTAL					
DINNER TIME:					
SUBTOTAL					
SNACKS TIME: / / /					
TOTAL					
vs. TARGET					

NOTES

_____

_____

_____

_____

HOW THE DAY WENT? ☐ BAD ☐ OK ☐ GOOD ☐ GREAT

DATE | |

S M T W T F S

WEIGHT
POUNDS/KILOS

SLEEP
HOURS

WATER
OZ/ml

HOW I FEEL ☺ ☺ ☺ ☹ **ENERGY** 🔋◁▭▭▭▭▷🔋 **ACTIVITY** 🛏️◁▭▭▭▷🏃

☐ SUGAR FREE ☐ ALCOHOL FREE ☐ GLUTEN FREE ☐ DAIRY FREE ☐ LOW CARB ☐ LOTS OF VEGGIES

☐ ORGANIC ☐ NO PROCESSED FOODS

BREAKFAST TIME:	SERVING SIZE	PROTEIN	FAT	CARBS	CALORIES
SUBTOTAL					

LUNCH TIME:					
SUBTOTAL					

DINNER TIME:					
SUBTOTAL					

SNACKS TIME: / / /					
TOTAL					
vs. TARGET					

NOTES

_____

_____

_____

_____

HOW THE DAY WENT? ☐ BAD ☐ OK ☐ GOOD ☐ GREAT

DATE | | ☐☐☐☐☐☐☐ **WEIGHT**   **SLEEP**   **WATER**
            S M T W T F S   POUNDS/KILOS   HOURS   OZ/ml

HOW I FEEL 😀 🙂 😐 🙁   **ENERGY** ▯▭▭▭▭▭▯🔋   **ACTIVITY** 🛏▭▭▭▭▭🏃

☐ SUGAR FREE   ☐ ALCOHOL FREE   ☐ GLUTEN FREE   ☐ DAIRY FREE   ☐ LOW CARB   ☐ LOTS OF VEGGIES
☐ ORGANIC   ☐ NO PROCESSED FOODS

BREAKFAST TIME:	SERVING SIZE	PROTEIN	FAT	CARBS	CALORIES
SUBTOTAL					

LUNCH TIME:					
SUBTOTAL					

DINNER TIME:					
SUBTOTAL					

SNACKS TIME: / / /					
TOTAL					
vs. TARGET					

NOTES
_____
_____
_____
_____

HOW THE DAY WENT? ☐ BAD ☐ OK ☐ GOOD ☐ GREAT

DATE | | | ☐☐☐☐☐☐☐ **WEIGHT** | **SLEEP** | **WATER**

S M T W T F S | POUNDS/KILOS | HOURS | OZ/ml

HOW I FEEL 😀 😊 😐 ☹ **ENERGY** ☐⊂▭▭▭▭▭⊃🔋 **ACTIVITY** 🛏⊂▭▭▭▭▭⊃🏃

☐ SUGAR FREE ☐ ALCOHOL FREE ☐ GLUTEN FREE ☐ DAIRY FREE ☐ LOW CARB ☐ LOTS OF VEGGIES

☐ ORGANIC ☐ NO PROCESSED FOODS

BREAKFAST TIME:	SERVING SIZE	PROTEIN	FAT	CARBS	CALORIES
SUBTOTAL					
LUNCH TIME:					
SUBTOTAL					
DINNER TIME:					
SUBTOTAL					
SNACKS TIME: / / /					
TOTAL					
vs. TARGET					

NOTES

_____

_____

_____

_____

HOW THE DAY WENT? ☐ BAD ☐ OK ☐ GOOD ☐ GREAT

DATE | | | ☐☐☐☐☐☐☐   **WEIGHT**   **SLEEP**   **WATER**
S M T W T F S   POUNDS/KILOS   HOURS   OZ/ml

HOW I FEEL 😄 🙂 😐 🙁   **ENERGY** 🔋▭▭▭▭▭ 🔋   **ACTIVITY** 🛏️▭▭▭▭ 🏃

☐ SUGAR FREE   ☐ ALCOHOL FREE   ☐ GLUTEN FREE   ☐ DAIRY FREE   ☐ LOW CARB   ☐ LOTS OF VEGGIES
☐ ORGANIC   ☐ NO PROCESSED FOODS

BREAKFAST TIME:	SERVING SIZE	PROTEIN	FAT	CARBS	CALORIES
SUBTOTAL					

LUNCH TIME:					
SUBTOTAL					

DINNER TIME:					
SUBTOTAL					

SNACKS TIME: / / /					
TOTAL					
vs. TARGET					

NOTES
_____
_____
_____
_____

HOW THE DAY WENT? [BAD] [OK] [GOOD] [GREAT]

DATE | |

S M T W T F S

WEIGHT
POUNDS/KILOS

SLEEP
HOURS

WATER
OZ/ml

HOW I FEEL 😄 🙂 😕 ☹️   **ENERGY** 🔋 ▭▭▭▭ 🔋   **ACTIVITY** 🛏️ ▭▭▭▭ 🏃

| | SUGAR FREE | | ALCOHOL FREE | | GLUTEN FREE | | DAIRY FREE | | LOW CARB | | LOTS OF VEGGIES |
| | ORGANIC | | NO PROCESSED FOODS | | | | | | | | |

BREAKFAST TIME:	SERVING SIZE	PROTEIN	FAT	CARBS	CALORIES
SUBTOTAL					
LUNCH TIME:					
SUBTOTAL					
DINNER TIME:					
SUBTOTAL					
SNACKS TIME: / / /					
TOTAL					
vs. TARGET					

NOTES

_____

_____

_____

_____

HOW THE DAY WENT? [BAD] [OK] [GOOD] [GREAT]

DATE | | | ☐☐☐☐☐☐ **WEIGHT** **SLEEP** **WATER**
S M T W T F S | POUNDS/KILOS | HOURS | OZ/ml

HOW I FEEL 😄 🙂 😐 ☹️ **ENERGY** 🔋⊏⊐⊐⊐⊐🔋 **ACTIVITY** 🛌⊏⊐⊐⊐⊐🏃

☐ SUGAR FREE   ☐ ALCOHOL FREE   ☐ GLUTEN FREE   ☐ DAIRY FREE   ☐ LOW CARB   ☐ LOTS OF VEGGIES
☐ ORGANIC   ☐ NO PROCESSED FOODS

BREAKFAST TIME:	SERVING SIZE	PROTEIN	FAT	CARBS	CALORIES
SUBTOTAL					
LUNCH TIME:					
SUBTOTAL					
DINNER TIME:					
SUBTOTAL					
SNACKS TIME: / / /					
TOTAL					
vs. TARGET					

NOTES
_____
_____
_____
_____

HOW THE DAY WENT? ☐ BAD ☐ OK ☐ GOOD ☐ GREAT

DATE | |

WEIGHT
POUNDS/KILOS

SLEEP
HOURS

WATER
OZ/ml

HOW I FEEL 😄 🙂 😐 🙁   ENERGY 🔋 ⫘⫘⫘⫘⫘ 🔋   ACTIVITY 🛏 ⫘⫘⫘⫘⫘ 🏃

☐ SUGAR FREE   ☐ ALCOHOL FREE   ☐ GLUTEN FREE   ☐ DAIRY FREE   ☐ LOW CARB   ☐ LOTS OF VEGGIES

☐ ORGANIC   ☐ NO PROCESSED FOODS

BREAKFAST TIME:	SERVING SIZE	PROTEIN	FAT	CARBS	CALORIES
SUBTOTAL					

LUNCH TIME:					
SUBTOTAL					

DINNER TIME:					
SUBTOTAL					

SNACKS TIME: / / /					
TOTAL					
vs. TARGET					

NOTES

_____

_____

_____

_____

HOW THE DAY WENT? ☐ BAD ☐ OK ☐ GOOD ☐ GREAT

DATE | | | ☐☐☐☐☐☐☐ S M T W T F S   **WEIGHT** POUNDS/KILOS   **SLEEP** HOURS   **WATER** OZ/ml

HOW I FEEL ☺ ☺ ☺ ☹   **ENERGY** ▯▭▭▭▭🔋   **ACTIVITY** 🛏▭▭▭▭🏃

☐ SUGAR FREE   ☐ ALCOHOL FREE   ☐ GLUTEN FREE   ☐ DAIRY FREE   ☐ LOW CARB   ☐ LOTS OF VEGGIES
☐ ORGANIC   ☐ NO PROCESSED FOODS

BREAKFAST TIME:	SERVING SIZE	PROTEIN	FAT	CARBS	CALORIES
SUBTOTAL					

LUNCH TIME:					
SUBTOTAL					

DINNER TIME:					
SUBTOTAL					

SNACKS TIME: / / /					
TOTAL					
vs. TARGET					

NOTES
_____
_____
_____
_____

HOW THE DAY WENT? ☐ BAD ☐ OK ☐ GOOD ☐ GREAT

DATE | |

S M T W T F S

WEIGHT
POUNDS/KILOS

SLEEP
HOURS

WATER
OZ/ml

HOW I FEEL 😀 🙂 😐 ☹️   **ENERGY** 🔋⊂▭▭▭⊃🔋   **ACTIVITY** 🛏⊂▭▭▭⊃🏃

- [ ] SUGAR FREE
- [ ] ALCOHOL FREE
- [ ] GLUTEN FREE
- [ ] DAIRY FREE
- [ ] LOW CARB
- [ ] LOTS OF VEGGIES
- [ ] ORGANIC
- [ ] NO PROCESSED FOODS

BREAKFAST TIME:	SERVING SIZE	PROTEIN	FAT	CARBS	CALORIES
SUBTOTAL					

LUNCH TIME:					
SUBTOTAL					

DINNER TIME:					
SUBTOTAL					

SNACKS TIME: / / /					
TOTAL					
vs. TARGET					

NOTES

_____

_____

_____

_____

HOW THE DAY WENT? BAD | OK | GOOD | GREAT

DATE | | ☐☐☐☐☐☐☐   **WEIGHT**   **SLEEP**   **WATER**
S M T W T F S   POUNDS/KILOS   HOURS   OZ/ml

HOW I FEEL 😄 🙂 😐 🙁   **ENERGY** 🔋 ⊏▭▭▭▭⊐ 🔋   **ACTIVITY** 🛏 ⊏▭▭▭▭⊐ 🏃

☐ SUGAR FREE   ☐ ALCOHOL FREE   ☐ GLUTEN FREE   ☐ DAIRY FREE   ☐ LOW CARB   ☐ LOTS OF VEGGIES
☐ ORGANIC   ☐ NO PROCESSED FOODS

BREAKFAST TIME:	SERVING SIZE	PROTEIN	FAT	CARBS	CALORIES
SUBTOTAL					

LUNCH TIME:					
SUBTOTAL					

DINNER TIME:					
SUBTOTAL					

SNACKS TIME: / / /					
TOTAL					
vs. TARGET					

NOTES
_____
_____
_____
_____

HOW THE DAY WENT? BAD   OK   GOOD   GREAT

DATE			☐ S ☐ M ☐ T ☐ W ☐ T ☐ F ☐ S	WEIGHT	SLEEP	WATER
				POUNDS/KILOS	HOURS	OZ/ml

HOW I FEEL 😄 ☺ 😐 ☹   **ENERGY** ▯━━━━▯ 🔋   **ACTIVITY** 🛏━━━━▭ 🏃

☐ SUGAR FREE ☐ ALCOHOL FREE ☐ GLUTEN FREE ☐ DAIRY FREE ☐ LOW CARB ☐ LOTS OF VEGGIES

☐ ORGANIC ☐ NO PROCESSED FOODS

BREAKFAST TIME:	SERVING SIZE	PROTEIN	FAT	CARBS	CALORIES
SUBTOTAL					
LUNCH TIME:					
SUBTOTAL					
DINNER TIME:					
SUBTOTAL					
SNACKS TIME: / / /					
TOTAL					
vs. TARGET					

NOTES

_____

_____

_____

_____

HOW THE DAY WENT? ☐ BAD ☐ OK ☐ GOOD ☐ GREAT

DATE | | | S M T W T F S | **WEIGHT** POUNDS/KILOS | **SLEEP** HOURS | **WATER** OZ/ml

HOW I FEEL ☺ ☺ ☺ ☹ **ENERGY** 🔋 ▭▭▭▭ 🔋 **ACTIVITY** 🛏 ▭▭▭▭ 🏃

☐ SUGAR FREE ☐ ALCOHOL FREE ☐ GLUTEN FREE ☐ DAIRY FREE ☐ LOW CARB ☐ LOTS OF VEGGIES
☐ ORGANIC ☐ NO PROCESSED FOODS

BREAKFAST TIME:	SERVING SIZE	PROTEIN	FAT	CARBS	CALORIES
SUBTOTAL					

LUNCH TIME:					
SUBTOTAL					

DINNER TIME:					
SUBTOTAL					

SNACKS TIME: / / /					
TOTAL					
vs. TARGET					

NOTES

_____
_____
_____

HOW THE DAY WENT? ☐ BAD ☐ OK ☐ GOOD ☐ GREAT

DATE | | | ☐☐☐☐☐☐☐ **WEIGHT** **SLEEP** **WATER**
S M T W T F S POUNDS/KILOS HOURS OZ/ml

HOW I FEEL ☺ ☺ ☹ ☹ **ENERGY** 🔋 ▭▭▭▭ 🔋 **ACTIVITY** 🛏 ▭▭▭▭ 🏃

☐ SUGAR FREE ☐ ALCOHOL FREE ☐ GLUTEN FREE ☐ DAIRY FREE ☐ LOW CARB ☐ LOTS OF VEGGIES
☐ ORGANIC ☐ NO PROCESSED FOODS

BREAKFAST TIME:	SERVING SIZE	PROTEIN	FAT	CARBS	CALORIES
SUBTOTAL					

LUNCH TIME:					
SUBTOTAL					

DINNER TIME:					
SUBTOTAL					

SNACKS TIME: / / /					
TOTAL					
vs. TARGET					

NOTES
_____
_____
_____
_____

HOW THE DAY WENT? ☐ BAD ☐ OK ☐ GOOD ☐ GREAT

DATE | | | ☐☐☐☐☐☐☐
S M T W T F S

WEIGHT
POUNDS/KILOS

SLEEP
HOURS

WATER
OZ/ml

HOW I FEEL ☺ ☺ ☺ ☹   ENERGY ☐⊏⊏⊏⊏⊐🔋   ACTIVITY 🛏⊏⊏⊏⊐🏃

☐ SUGAR FREE   ☐ ALCOHOL FREE   ☐ GLUTEN FREE   ☐ DAIRY FREE   ☐ LOW CARB   ☐ LOTS OF VEGGIES
☐ ORGANIC   ☐ NO PROCESSED FOODS

BREAKFAST TIME:	SERVING SIZE	PROTEIN	FAT	CARBS	CALORIES
SUBTOTAL					

LUNCH TIME:					
SUBTOTAL					

DINNER TIME:					
SUBTOTAL					

SNACKS TIME: / / /					
TOTAL					
vs. TARGET					

NOTES
_____
_____
_____
_____

HOW THE DAY WENT? ☐ BAD ☐ OK ☐ GOOD ☐ GREAT

DATE | | | □□□□□□□ **WEIGHT** | **SLEEP** | **WATER**
S M T W T F S | POUNDS/KILOS | HOURS | OZ/ml

HOW I FEEL 😃 🙂 😐 ☹️ **ENERGY** 🔋 ⊂▭▭▭▭▭⊃ 🔋 **ACTIVITY** 🛏 ⊂▭▭▭▭⊃ 🏃

☐ SUGAR FREE ☐ ALCOHOL FREE ☐ GLUTEN FREE ☐ DAIRY FREE ☐ LOW CARB ☐ LOTS OF VEGGIES
☐ ORGANIC ☐ NO PROCESSED FOODS

BREAKFAST TIME:	SERVING SIZE	PROTEIN	FAT	CARBS	CALORIES
SUBTOTAL					
LUNCH TIME:					
SUBTOTAL					
DINNER TIME:					
SUBTOTAL					
SNACKS TIME: / / /					
TOTAL					
vs. TARGET					

NOTES

_____
_____
_____
_____

HOW THE DAY WENT? ☐ BAD ☐ OK ☐ GOOD ☐ GREAT

DATE				S M T W T F S	WEIGHT	SLEEP	WATER
					POUNDS/KILOS	HOURS	OZ/ml

HOW I FEEL ☺ ☺ ☺ ☹   ENERGY 🔋⊏⊐⊐⊐⊐🔋   ACTIVITY 🛏⊏⊐⊐⊐🏃

☐ SUGAR FREE   ☐ ALCOHOL FREE   ☐ GLUTEN FREE   ☐ DAIRY FREE   ☐ LOW CARB   ☐ LOTS OF VEGGIES
☐ ORGANIC   ☐ NO PROCESSED FOODS

BREAKFAST TIME:	SERVING SIZE	PROTEIN	FAT	CARBS	CALORIES
SUBTOTAL					

LUNCH TIME:					
SUBTOTAL					

DINNER TIME:					
SUBTOTAL					

SNACKS TIME: / / /					
TOTAL					
vs. TARGET					

NOTES
_____
_____
_____
_____

HOW THE DAY WENT? ☐ BAD ☐ OK ☐ GOOD ☐ GREAT

DATE			☐☐☐☐☐☐☐	WEIGHT	SLEEP	WATER
			S M T W T F S	POUNDS/KILOS	HOURS	OZ/ml

HOW I FEEL 😃 ☺ 😐 ☹ ENERGY ☐▭▭▭▭🔋 ACTIVITY 🛏▭▭▭▭🏃

☐ SUGAR FREE ☐ ALCOHOL FREE ☐ GLUTEN FREE ☐ DAIRY FREE ☐ LOW CARB ☐ LOTS OF VEGGIES
☐ ORGANIC ☐ NO PROCESSED FOODS

BREAKFAST TIME:	SERVING SIZE	PROTEIN	FAT	CARBS	CALORIES
SUBTOTAL					

LUNCH TIME:					
SUBTOTAL					

DINNER TIME:					
SUBTOTAL					

SNACKS TIME: / / /					
TOTAL					
vs. TARGET					

NOTES

_____

_____

_____

_____

HOW THE DAY WENT? ☐ BAD ☐ OK ☐ GOOD ☐ GREAT

| DATE | | | | | S M T W T F S | **WEIGHT** POUNDS/KILOS | **SLEEP** HOURS | **WATER** OZ/ml |

DATE | | | □□□□□□□ S M T W T F S   **WEIGHT** POUNDS/KILOS   **SLEEP** HOURS   **WATER** OZ/ml

HOW I FEEL ☺ ☺ ☺ ☹   **ENERGY** ▯ ⊏⊐⊐⊐⊐ 🔋   **ACTIVITY** 🛏 ⊏⊐⊐⊐⊐ 🏃

☐ SUGAR FREE   ☐ ALCOHOL FREE   ☐ GLUTEN FREE   ☐ DAIRY FREE   ☐ LOW CARB   ☐ LOTS OF VEGGIES
☐ ORGANIC   ☐ NO PROCESSED FOODS

BREAKFAST TIME:	SERVING SIZE	PROTEIN	FAT	CARBS	CALORIES
SUBTOTAL					
LUNCH TIME:					
SUBTOTAL					
DINNER TIME:					
SUBTOTAL					
SNACKS TIME: / / /					
TOTAL					
vs. TARGET					

NOTES
_____
_____
_____
_____

HOW THE DAY WENT? ☐ BAD ☐ OK ☐ GOOD ☐ GREAT

DATE | | | | ☐☐☐☐☐☐   **WEIGHT**   **SLEEP**   **WATER**

S M T W T F S   POUNDS/KILOS   HOURS   OZ/ml

HOW I FEEL 😄 🙂 😐 ☹️   **ENERGY** ▯ ☐☐☐☐ 🔋   **ACTIVITY** 🛏 ☐☐☐☐ 🏃

☐ SUGAR FREE   ☐ ALCOHOL FREE   ☐ GLUTEN FREE   ☐ DAIRY FREE   ☐ LOW CARB   ☐ LOTS OF VEGGIES

☐ ORGANIC   ☐ NO PROCESSED FOODS

BREAKFAST TIME:	SERVING SIZE	PROTEIN	FAT	CARBS	CALORIES
SUBTOTAL					
LUNCH TIME:					
SUBTOTAL					
DINNER TIME:					
SUBTOTAL					
SNACKS TIME: / / /					
TOTAL					
vs. TARGET					

NOTES

_____

_____

_____

_____

HOW THE DAY WENT? ☐ BAD ☐ OK ☐ GOOD ☐ GREAT

DATE | |

S M T W T F S

WEIGHT POUNDS/KILOS

SLEEP HOURS

WATER OZ/ml

HOW I FEEL ☺ ☺ ☺ ☹　**ENERGY** 🔋⊏⊏⊏⊏⊐🔋　**ACTIVITY** 🛏⊏⊏⊏⊐🏃

☐ SUGAR FREE　☐ ALCOHOL FREE　☐ GLUTEN FREE　☐ DAIRY FREE　☐ LOW CARB　☐ LOTS OF VEGGIES
☐ ORGANIC　☐ NO PROCESSED FOODS

BREAKFAST TIME:	SERVING SIZE	PROTEIN	FAT	CARBS	CALORIES
SUBTOTAL					
LUNCH TIME:					
SUBTOTAL					
DINNER TIME:					
SUBTOTAL					
SNACKS TIME: / / /					
TOTAL					
vs. TARGET					

NOTES

_____
_____
_____
_____

HOW THE DAY WENT? ☐ BAD　☐ OK　☐ GOOD　☐ GREAT

DATE | |

S M T W T F S

WEIGHT
POUNDS/KILOS

SLEEP
HOURS

WATER
OZ/ml

HOW I FEEL 😁 ☺ 😐 ☹   ENERGY 🔋 ⊂▭▭▭▭⊃ 🔋   ACTIVITY 🛏 ⊂▭▭▭▭⊃ 🏃

☐ SUGAR FREE ☐ ALCOHOL FREE ☐ GLUTEN FREE ☐ DAIRY FREE ☐ LOW CARB ☐ LOTS OF VEGGIES

☐ ORGANIC ☐ NO PROCESSED FOODS

BREAKFAST TIME:	SERVING SIZE	PROTEIN	FAT	CARBS	CALORIES
SUBTOTAL					

LUNCH TIME:					
SUBTOTAL					

DINNER TIME:					
SUBTOTAL					

SNACKS TIME: / / /					
TOTAL					
vs. TARGET					

NOTES

_____

_____

_____

_____

HOW THE DAY WENT? [BAD] [OK] [GOOD] [GREAT]

DATE | | | □□□□□□□ WEIGHT SLEEP WATER
S M T W T F S POUNDS/KILOS HOURS OZ/ml

HOW I FEEL ☺ ☺ ☺ ☹   ENERGY 🔋▭▭▭▭▭🔋   ACTIVITY 🛏▭▭▭▭▭🏃

☐ SUGAR FREE   ☐ ALCOHOL FREE   ☐ GLUTEN FREE   ☐ DAIRY FREE   ☐ LOW CARB   ☐ LOTS OF VEGGIES
☐ ORGANIC   ☐ NO PROCESSED FOODS

BREAKFAST TIME:	SERVING SIZE	PROTEIN	FAT	CARBS	CALORIES
SUBTOTAL					
LUNCH TIME:					
SUBTOTAL					
DINNER TIME:					
SUBTOTAL					
SNACKS TIME: / / /					
TOTAL					
vs. TARGET					

NOTES
_____
_____
_____
_____

HOW THE DAY WENT? [BAD] [OK] [GOOD] [GREAT]

DATE | |

☐☐☐☐☐☐☐
S M T W T F S

WEIGHT
POUNDS/KILOS

SLEEP
HOURS

WATER
OZ/ml

HOW I FEEL 😃 ☺ 😐 ☹   **ENERGY** 🔋▭▭▭▭🔋   **ACTIVITY** 🛏▭▭▭🏃

☐ SUGAR FREE   ☐ ALCOHOL FREE   ☐ GLUTEN FREE   ☐ DAIRY FREE   ☐ LOW CARB   ☐ LOTS OF VEGGIES

☐ ORGANIC   ☐ NO PROCESSED FOODS

BREAKFAST TIME:	SERVING SIZE	PROTEIN	FAT	CARBS	CALORIES
SUBTOTAL					
LUNCH TIME:					
SUBTOTAL					
DINNER TIME:					
SUBTOTAL					
SNACKS TIME: / / /					
TOTAL					
vs. TARGET					

NOTES

_____

_____

_____

_____

HOW THE DAY WENT? ☐ BAD ☐ OK ☐ GOOD ☐ GREAT

DATE | | | ☐☐☐☐☐☐☐ **WEIGHT**   **SLEEP**   **WATER**

S M T W T F S   POUNDS/KILOS   HOURS   OZ/ml

HOW I FEEL ☺ ☺ ☺ ☹   **ENERGY** ▯ ⊂━━━▭ 🔋   **ACTIVITY** 🛏 ⊂━━━▭ 🏃

☐ SUGAR FREE   ☐ ALCOHOL FREE   ☐ GLUTEN FREE   ☐ DAIRY FREE   ☐ LOW CARB   ☐ LOTS OF VEGGIES

☐ ORGANIC   ☐ NO PROCESSED FOODS

BREAKFAST TIME:	SERVING SIZE	PROTEIN	FAT	CARBS	CALORIES
SUBTOTAL					
LUNCH TIME:					
SUBTOTAL					
DINNER TIME:					
SUBTOTAL					
SNACKS TIME: / / /					
TOTAL					
vs. TARGET					

NOTES

_____

_____

_____

_____

HOW THE DAY WENT? ☐ BAD   ☐ OK   ☐ GOOD   ☐ GREAT

DATE | | | □□□□□□□
S M T W T F S

WEIGHT
POUNDS/KILOS

SLEEP
HOURS

WATER
OZ/ml

HOW I FEEL 😀 🙂 😐 ☹️   **ENERGY** 🔋 ▭▭▭▭ 🔋   **ACTIVITY** 🛏️ ▭▭▭▭ 🏃

☐ SUGAR FREE   ☐ ALCOHOL FREE   ☐ GLUTEN FREE   ☐ DAIRY FREE   ☐ LOW CARB   ☐ LOTS OF VEGGIES
☐ ORGANIC   ☐ NO PROCESSED FOODS

BREAKFAST TIME:	SERVING SIZE	PROTEIN	FAT	CARBS	CALORIES
SUBTOTAL					

LUNCH TIME:					
SUBTOTAL					

DINNER TIME:					
SUBTOTAL					

SNACKS TIME: / / /					
TOTAL					
vs. TARGET					

NOTES
_____
_____
_____
_____

HOW THE DAY WENT? ☐ BAD ☐ OK ☐ GOOD ☐ GREAT

| DATE | | | | S M T W T F S | WEIGHT POUNDS/KILOS | SLEEP HOURS | WATER OZ/ml |

HOW I FEEL ☺ ☺ ☺ ☹ **ENERGY** ▯▭▭▭▭ ▮ **ACTIVITY** 🛏 ▭▭▭▭ 🏃

☐ SUGAR FREE ☐ ALCOHOL FREE ☐ GLUTEN FREE ☐ DAIRY FREE ☐ LOW CARB ☐ LOTS OF VEGGIES
☐ ORGANIC ☐ NO PROCESSED FOODS

BREAKFAST TIME:	SERVING SIZE	PROTEIN	FAT	CARBS	CALORIES
SUBTOTAL					
LUNCH TIME:					
SUBTOTAL					
DINNER TIME:					
SUBTOTAL					
SNACKS TIME: / / /					
TOTAL					
vs. TARGET					

NOTES

_____
_____
_____
_____

HOW THE DAY WENT? [BAD] [OK] [GOOD] [GREAT]

DATE | | ☐☐☐☐☐☐   👤 **WEIGHT**   💤 **SLEEP**   💧 **WATER**

S M T W T F S   POUNDS/KILOS   HOURS   OZ/ml

HOW I FEEL 😄 🙂 😐 ☹️   **ENERGY** 🔋⬜⬜⬜⬜🔋   **ACTIVITY** 🛏️⬜⬜⬜⬜ 🏃

☐ SUGAR FREE   ☐ ALCOHOL FREE   ☐ GLUTEN FREE   ☐ DAIRY FREE   ☐ LOW CARB   ☐ LOTS OF VEGGIES

☐ ORGANIC   ☐ NO PROCESSED FOODS

BREAKFAST TIME:	SERVING SIZE	PROTEIN	FAT	CARBS	CALORIES
SUBTOTAL					
LUNCH TIME:					
SUBTOTAL					
DINNER TIME:					
SUBTOTAL					
SNACKS TIME: / / /					
TOTAL					
vs. TARGET					

NOTES

_____

_____

_____

_____

HOW THE DAY WENT? ☐ BAD ☐ OK ☐ GOOD ☐ GREAT

| DATE | | | S M T W T F S | WEIGHT POUNDS/KILOS | SLEEP HOURS | WATER OZ/ml |

HOW I FEEL 😄 🙂 😐 ☹️   **ENERGY** 🔋 ⬜⬜⬜⬜ 🔋   **ACTIVITY** 🛏️ ⬜⬜⬜⬜ 🏃

| | SUGAR FREE | | ALCOHOL FREE | | GLUTEN FREE | | DAIRY FREE | | LOW CARB | | LOTS OF VEGGIES |
| | ORGANIC | | NO PROCESSED FOODS |

BREAKFAST TIME:	SERVING SIZE	PROTEIN	FAT	CARBS	CALORIES
SUBTOTAL					
LUNCH TIME:					
SUBTOTAL					
DINNER TIME:					
SUBTOTAL					
SNACKS TIME: / / /					
TOTAL					
vs. TARGET					

NOTES

_____
_____
_____
_____

HOW THE DAY WENT? [BAD] [OK] [GOOD] [GREAT]

DATE | | | ☐☐☐☐☐☐☐
S M T W T F S

WEIGHT
POUNDS/KILOS

SLEEP
HOURS

WATER
OZ/ml

HOW I FEEL 😀 ☺ 😐 ☹   **ENERGY** 🔋▭▭▭▭🔋   **ACTIVITY** 🛏▭▭▭▭🏃

☐ SUGAR FREE ☐ ALCOHOL FREE ☐ GLUTEN FREE ☐ DAIRY FREE ☐ LOW CARB ☐ LOTS OF VEGGIES
☐ ORGANIC ☐ NO PROCESSED FOODS

BREAKFAST TIME:	SERVING SIZE	PROTEIN	FAT	CARBS	CALORIES
SUBTOTAL					

LUNCH TIME:					
SUBTOTAL					

DINNER TIME:					
SUBTOTAL					

SNACKS TIME: / / /					
TOTAL					
vs. TARGET					

NOTES
_____
_____
_____
_____

HOW THE DAY WENT? [BAD] [OK] [GOOD] [GREAT]

DATE | | | ☐☐☐☐☐☐☐ **WEIGHT** **SLEEP** **WATER**
S M T W T F S

POUNDS/KILOS   HOURS   OZ/ml

HOW I FEEL 😄 🙂 😐 🙁   ENERGY ▯▭▭▭▭▭ 🔋   ACTIVITY 🛏▭▭▭▭ 🏃

☐ SUGAR FREE ☐ ALCOHOL FREE ☐ GLUTEN FREE ☐ DAIRY FREE ☐ LOW CARB ☐ LOTS OF VEGGIES

☐ ORGANIC ☐ NO PROCESSED FOODS

BREAKFAST TIME:	SERVING SIZE	PROTEIN	FAT	CARBS	CALORIES
SUBTOTAL					
LUNCH TIME:					
SUBTOTAL					
DINNER TIME:					
SUBTOTAL					
SNACKS TIME: / / /					
TOTAL					
vs. TARGET					

NOTES

_____

_____

_____

_____

HOW THE DAY WENT? ☐ BAD ☐ OK ☐ GOOD ☐ GREAT

DATE | | | ☐☐☐☐☐☐☐
S M T W T F S

WEIGHT 🏋
POUNDS/KILOS

SLEEP 😴
HOURS

WATER 💧
OZ/ml

HOW I FEEL 😄 🙂 😐 ☹️   **ENERGY** 🔋⊏▭▭▭⊐🔋   **ACTIVITY** 🛏⊏▭▭▭⊐🏃

☐ SUGAR FREE   ☐ ALCOHOL FREE   ☐ GLUTEN FREE   ☐ DAIRY FREE   ☐ LOW CARB   ☐ LOTS OF VEGGIES

☐ ORGANIC   ☐ NO PROCESSED FOODS

BREAKFAST TIME:	SERVING SIZE	PROTEIN	FAT	CARBS	CALORIES
SUBTOTAL					
LUNCH TIME:					
SUBTOTAL					
DINNER TIME:					
SUBTOTAL					
SNACKS TIME: / / /					
TOTAL					
vs. TARGET					

NOTES

_____

_____

_____

HOW THE DAY WENT? ☐ BAD ☐ OK ☐ GOOD ☐ GREAT

DATE			S M T W T F S	**WEIGHT**	**SLEEP**	**WATER**
				POUNDS/KILOS	HOURS	OZ/ml

HOW I FEEL 😄 🙂 😐 🙁 **ENERGY** ▭▭▭▭▭🔋 **ACTIVITY** 🛏▭▭▭🏃

☐ SUGAR FREE ☐ ALCOHOL FREE ☐ GLUTEN FREE ☐ DAIRY FREE ☐ LOW CARB ☐ LOTS OF VEGGIES
☐ ORGANIC ☐ NO PROCESSED FOODS

BREAKFAST TIME:	SERVING SIZE	PROTEIN	FAT	CARBS	CALORIES
SUBTOTAL					
LUNCH TIME:					
SUBTOTAL					
DINNER TIME:					
SUBTOTAL					
SNACKS TIME: / / /					
TOTAL					
vs. TARGET					

NOTES

_____
_____
_____
_____

HOW THE DAY WENT? ☐ BAD ☐ OK ☐ GOOD ☐ GREAT

DATE | |

S M T W T F S

WEIGHT — POUNDS/KILOS

SLEEP — HOURS

WATER — OZ/ml

HOW I FEEL ☺ ☺ ☺ ☹   **ENERGY** 🔋▭▭▭▭🔋   **ACTIVITY** 🛏▭▭▭🏃

☐ SUGAR FREE   ☐ ALCOHOL FREE   ☐ GLUTEN FREE   ☐ DAIRY FREE   ☐ LOW CARB   ☐ LOTS OF VEGGIES

☐ ORGANIC   ☐ NO PROCESSED FOODS

BREAKFAST TIME:	SERVING SIZE	PROTEIN	FAT	CARBS	CALORIES
SUBTOTAL					
LUNCH TIME:					
SUBTOTAL					
DINNER TIME:					
SUBTOTAL					
SNACKS TIME: / / /					
TOTAL					
vs. TARGET					

NOTES

_____

_____

_____

_____

HOW THE DAY WENT? ☐ BAD ☐ OK ☐ GOOD ☐ GREAT

DATE | | _____ SMTWTFS

WEIGHT
POUNDS/KILOS

SLEEP
HOURS

WATER
OZ/ml

HOW I FEEL ☺ ☺ ☺ ☹   **ENERGY** ▯▭▭▭▭▭ 🔋   **ACTIVITY** 🛏▭▭▭▭ 🏃

☐ SUGAR FREE   ☐ ALCOHOL FREE   ☐ GLUTEN FREE   ☐ DAIRY FREE   ☐ LOW CARB   ☐ LOTS OF VEGGIES
☐ ORGANIC   ☐ NO PROCESSED FOODS

BREAKFAST TIME:	SERVING SIZE	PROTEIN	FAT	CARBS	CALORIES
SUBTOTAL					

LUNCH TIME:					
SUBTOTAL					

DINNER TIME:					
SUBTOTAL					

SNACKS TIME: / / /					
TOTAL					
vs. TARGET					

NOTES
_____
_____
_____
_____

HOW THE DAY WENT? ☐ BAD ☐ OK ☐ GOOD ☐ GREAT

DATE | | ☐☐☐☐☐☐ **WEIGHT**   **SLEEP**   **WATER**

S M T W T F S   POUNDS/KILOS   HOURS   OZ/ml

HOW I FEEL 😄 🙂 😐 ☹️   **ENERGY** 🔋▭▭▭▭▭🔋   **ACTIVITY** 🛏️▭▭▭▭🏃

☐ SUGAR FREE ☐ ALCOHOL FREE ☐ GLUTEN FREE ☐ DAIRY FREE ☐ LOW CARB ☐ LOTS OF VEGGIES

☐ ORGANIC ☐ NO PROCESSED FOODS

BREAKFAST TIME:	SERVING SIZE	PROTEIN	FAT	CARBS	CALORIES
SUBTOTAL					
LUNCH TIME:					
SUBTOTAL					
DINNER TIME:					
SUBTOTAL					
SNACKS TIME: / / /					
TOTAL					
vs. TARGET					

NOTES

_____

_____

_____

_____

HOW THE DAY WENT? ☐ BAD ☐ OK ☐ GOOD ☐ GREAT

DATE | | S M T W T F S

WEIGHT POUNDS/KILOS | **SLEEP** HOURS | **WATER** OZ/ml

HOW I FEEL ☺ ☺ ☺ ☹   **ENERGY** 🔋   **ACTIVITY** 🏃

☐ SUGAR FREE   ☐ ALCOHOL FREE   ☐ GLUTEN FREE   ☐ DAIRY FREE   ☐ LOW CARB   ☐ LOTS OF VEGGIES
☐ ORGANIC   ☐ NO PROCESSED FOODS

BREAKFAST TIME:	SERVING SIZE	PROTEIN	FAT	CARBS	CALORIES
SUBTOTAL					

LUNCH TIME:					
SUBTOTAL					

DINNER TIME:					
SUBTOTAL					

SNACKS TIME: / / /					
TOTAL					
vs. TARGET					

NOTES
_____
_____
_____
_____

HOW THE DAY WENT? ☐ BAD ☐ OK ☐ GOOD ☐ GREAT

DATE | |

S M T W T F S

WEIGHT
POUNDS/KILOS

SLEEP
HOURS

WATER
OZ/ml

HOW I FEEL ☺ ☺ ☺ ☹   **ENERGY** 🔋 ▭▭▭▭ 🔋   **ACTIVITY** 🛏 ▭▭▭ 🏃

- [ ] SUGAR FREE
- [ ] ALCOHOL FREE
- [ ] GLUTEN FREE
- [ ] DAIRY FREE
- [ ] LOW CARB
- [ ] LOTS OF VEGGIES
- [ ] ORGANIC
- [ ] NO PROCESSED FOODS

BREAKFAST TIME:	SERVING SIZE	PROTEIN	FAT	CARBS	CALORIES
SUBTOTAL					
LUNCH TIME:					
SUBTOTAL					
DINNER TIME:					
SUBTOTAL					
SNACKS TIME: / / /					
TOTAL					
vs. TARGET					

NOTES

_____

_____

_____

HOW THE DAY WENT? | BAD | OK | GOOD | GREAT |

DATE | | | ☐☐☐☐☐☐☐ **WEIGHT** **SLEEP** **WATER**

S M T W T F S

POUNDS/KILOS   HOURS   OZ/ml

HOW I FEEL 😄 🙂 😐 ☹   **ENERGY** ▯ ⊏⊏⊏⊏⊐ ▮   **ACTIVITY** 🛏 ⊏⊏⊏⊏⊐ 🏃

☐ SUGAR FREE ☐ ALCOHOL FREE ☐ GLUTEN FREE ☐ DAIRY FREE ☐ LOW CARB ☐ LOTS OF VEGGIES

☐ ORGANIC ☐ NO PROCESSED FOODS

BREAKFAST TIME:	SERVING SIZE	PROTEIN	FAT	CARBS	CALORIES
SUBTOTAL					
LUNCH TIME:					
SUBTOTAL					
DINNER TIME:					
SUBTOTAL					
SNACKS TIME: / / /					
TOTAL					
vs. TARGET					

NOTES

_____

_____

_____

_____

HOW THE DAY WENT? ☐ BAD ☐ OK ☐ GOOD ☐ GREAT

DATE | | | ☐☐☐☐☐☐☐ **WEIGHT** **SLEEP** **WATER**
S M T W T F S POUNDS/KILOS HOURS OZ/ml

HOW I FEEL ☺ ☺ ☹ ☹ **ENERGY** 🔋▭▭▭▭▭🔋 **ACTIVITY** 🛏▭▭▭▭ 🏃

☐ SUGAR FREE ☐ ALCOHOL FREE ☐ GLUTEN FREE ☐ DAIRY FREE ☐ LOW CARB ☐ LOTS OF VEGGIES
☐ ORGANIC ☐ NO PROCESSED FOODS

BREAKFAST TIME:	SERVING SIZE	PROTEIN	FAT	CARBS	CALORIES
SUBTOTAL					

LUNCH TIME:					
SUBTOTAL					

DINNER TIME:					
SUBTOTAL					

SNACKS TIME: / / /					
TOTAL					
vs. TARGET					

NOTES
_____
_____
_____

HOW THE DAY WENT? ☐ BAD ☐ OK ☐ GOOD ☐ GREAT

DATE | | | ☐☐☐☐☐☐☐   **WEIGHT**   **SLEEP**   **WATER**

S M T W T F S   POUNDS/KILOS   HOURS   OZ/ml

HOW I FEEL 😄 🙂 😐 🙁   **ENERGY** 🔋▭▭▭▭▭🔋   **ACTIVITY** 🛏▭▭▭▭🏃

☐ SUGAR FREE   ☐ ALCOHOL FREE   ☐ GLUTEN FREE   ☐ DAIRY FREE   ☐ LOW CARB   ☐ LOTS OF VEGGIES

☐ ORGANIC   ☐ NO PROCESSED FOODS

BREAKFAST TIME:	SERVING SIZE	PROTEIN	FAT	CARBS	CALORIES
SUBTOTAL					

LUNCH TIME:					
SUBTOTAL					

DINNER TIME:					
SUBTOTAL					

SNACKS TIME: / / /					
TOTAL					
vs. TARGET					

NOTES

_____

_____

_____

_____

HOW THE DAY WENT? ☐ BAD ☐ OK ☐ GOOD ☐ GREAT

DATE | | | ☐☐☐☐☐☐☐
S M T W T F S

WEIGHT
POUNDS/KILOS

SLEEP
HOURS

WATER
OZ/ml

HOW I FEEL ☺ ☺ ☹ ☹   ENERGY ☐▭▭▭▭▭🔋   ACTIVITY 🛏▭▭▭▭🏃

☐ SUGAR FREE   ☐ ALCOHOL FREE   ☐ GLUTEN FREE   ☐ DAIRY FREE   ☐ LOW CARB   ☐ LOTS OF VEGGIES
☐ ORGANIC   ☐ NO PROCESSED FOODS

BREAKFAST TIME:	SERVING SIZE	PROTEIN	FAT	CARBS	CALORIES
SUBTOTAL					
LUNCH TIME:					
SUBTOTAL					
DINNER TIME:					
SUBTOTAL					
SNACKS TIME: / / /					
TOTAL					
vs. TARGET					

NOTES

_____

_____

_____

_____

HOW THE DAY WENT? ☐ BAD ☐ OK ☐ GOOD ☐ GREAT

DATE | | | □□□□□□□ **WEIGHT**   **SLEEP**   **WATER**

S M T W T F S   POUNDS/KILOS   HOURS   OZ/ml

HOW I FEEL 😀 🙂 😐 🙁   **ENERGY** ▯▭▭▭▭ 🔋   **ACTIVITY** 🛏▭▭▭▭ 🏃

☐ SUGAR FREE ☐ ALCOHOL FREE ☐ GLUTEN FREE ☐ DAIRY FREE ☐ LOW CARB ☐ LOTS OF VEGGIES

☐ ORGANIC ☐ NO PROCESSED FOODS

BREAKFAST TIME:	SERVING SIZE	PROTEIN	FAT	CARBS	CALORIES
SUBTOTAL					
LUNCH TIME:					
SUBTOTAL					
DINNER TIME:					
SUBTOTAL					
SNACKS TIME: / / /					
TOTAL					
vs. TARGET					

NOTES

_____

_____

_____

_____

HOW THE DAY WENT? [BAD] [OK] [GOOD] [GREAT]

DATE | | | ☐☐☐☐☐☐☐ | **WEIGHT** | **SLEEP** | **WATER**
S M T W T F S | POUNDS/KILOS | HOURS | OZ/ml

HOW I FEEL 😄 🙂 😐 🙁   **ENERGY** 🔋▭▭▭▭🔋   **ACTIVITY** 🛏▭▭▭▭🏃

☐ SUGAR FREE ☐ ALCOHOL FREE ☐ GLUTEN FREE ☐ DAIRY FREE ☐ LOW CARB ☐ LOTS OF VEGGIES
☐ ORGANIC ☐ NO PROCESSED FOODS

BREAKFAST TIME:	SERVING SIZE	PROTEIN	FAT	CARBS	CALORIES
SUBTOTAL					

LUNCH TIME:					
SUBTOTAL					

DINNER TIME:					
SUBTOTAL					

SNACKS TIME: / / /					
TOTAL					
vs. TARGET					

NOTES
_____
_____
_____
_____

HOW THE DAY WENT? ☐ BAD ☐ OK ☐ GOOD ☐ GREAT

DATE | | SMTWTFS **WEIGHT** POUNDS/KILOS **SLEEP** HOURS **WATER** OZ/ml

HOW I FEEL 😄 🙂 😐 🙁 **ENERGY** 🔋 ▭▭▭▭▭ 🔋 **ACTIVITY** 🛏 ▭▭▭▭ 🏃

☐ SUGAR FREE ☐ ALCOHOL FREE ☐ GLUTEN FREE ☐ DAIRY FREE ☐ LOW CARB ☐ LOTS OF VEGGIES
☐ ORGANIC ☐ NO PROCESSED FOODS

BREAKFAST TIME:	SERVING SIZE	PROTEIN	FAT	CARBS	CALORIES
SUBTOTAL					
LUNCH TIME:					
SUBTOTAL					
DINNER TIME:					
SUBTOTAL					
SNACKS TIME: / / /					
TOTAL					
vs. TARGET					

NOTES

_____

_____

_____

_____

HOW THE DAY WENT? BAD | OK | GOOD | GREAT

DATE | | | ☐☐☐☐☐☐ **WEIGHT** **SLEEP** **WATER**
S M T W T F S | POUNDS/KILOS | HOURS | OZ/ml

HOW I FEEL 😃 🙂 😐 ☹️ **ENERGY** 🔋▢▭▭▭▭🔋 **ACTIVITY** 🛏️▭▭▭▭🏃

☐ SUGAR FREE   ☐ ALCOHOL FREE   ☐ GLUTEN FREE   ☐ DAIRY FREE   ☐ LOW CARB   ☐ LOTS OF VEGGIES
☐ ORGANIC   ☐ NO PROCESSED FOODS

BREAKFAST TIME:	SERVING SIZE	PROTEIN	FAT	CARBS	CALORIES
SUBTOTAL					
LUNCH TIME:					
SUBTOTAL					
DINNER TIME:					
SUBTOTAL					
SNACKS TIME: / / /					
TOTAL					
vs. TARGET					

NOTES

_____

_____

_____

_____

HOW THE DAY WENT? ☐ BAD ☐ OK ☐ GOOD ☐ GREAT

DATE | | | ☐☐☐☐☐☐☐ S M T W T F S | **WEIGHT** _____ POUNDS/KILOS | **SLEEP** _____ HOURS | **WATER** _____ OZ/ml

HOW I FEEL 😄 🙂 😐 ☹️   **ENERGY** 🔋▢▭▭▭▭▭▯🔋   **ACTIVITY** 🛏️▭▭▭▭▭▯🏃

☐ SUGAR FREE   ☐ ALCOHOL FREE   ☐ GLUTEN FREE   ☐ DAIRY FREE   ☐ LOW CARB   ☐ LOTS OF VEGGIES
☐ ORGANIC   ☐ NO PROCESSED FOODS

BREAKFAST TIME:	SERVING SIZE	PROTEIN	FAT	CARBS	CALORIES
SUBTOTAL					
LUNCH TIME:					
SUBTOTAL					
DINNER TIME:					
SUBTOTAL					
SNACKS TIME: / / /					
TOTAL					
vs. TARGET					

NOTES

_____
_____
_____
_____

HOW THE DAY WENT? ☐ BAD ☐ OK ☐ GOOD ☐ GREAT

DATE | | □□□□□□□

WEIGHT
POUNDS/KILOS

SLEEP
HOURS

WATER
OZ/ml

S M T W T F S

HOW I FEEL ☺ ☺ ☺ ☹   **ENERGY** ▯ ▭▭▭▭ 🔋   **ACTIVITY** 🛏 ▭▭▭▭ 🏃

☐ SUGAR FREE ☐ ALCOHOL FREE ☐ GLUTEN FREE ☐ DAIRY FREE ☐ LOW CARB ☐ LOTS OF VEGGIES
☐ ORGANIC ☐ NO PROCESSED FOODS

BREAKFAST TIME:	SERVING SIZE	PROTEIN	FAT	CARBS	CALORIES
SUBTOTAL					
LUNCH TIME:					
SUBTOTAL					
DINNER TIME:					
SUBTOTAL					
SNACKS TIME: / / /					
TOTAL					
vs. TARGET					

NOTES

_____
_____
_____
_____

HOW THE DAY WENT? ☐ BAD ☐ OK ☐ GOOD ☐ GREAT

DATE | | | ☐☐☐☐☐☐☐
S M T W T F S

WEIGHT
POUNDS/KILOS

SLEEP
HOURS

WATER
OZ/ml

HOW I FEEL 😄 🙂 😐 🙁   ENERGY 🔋 ⬜⬜⬜⬜⬜ 🔋   ACTIVITY 🛏 ⬜⬜⬜⬜⬜ 🏃

☐ SUGAR FREE   ☐ ALCOHOL FREE   ☐ GLUTEN FREE   ☐ DAIRY FREE   ☐ LOW CARB   ☐ LOTS OF VEGGIES
☐ ORGANIC   ☐ NO PROCESSED FOODS

BREAKFAST TIME:	SERVING SIZE	PROTEIN	FAT	CARBS	CALORIES
SUBTOTAL					

LUNCH TIME:					
SUBTOTAL					

DINNER TIME:					
SUBTOTAL					

SNACKS TIME: / / /					
TOTAL					
vs. TARGET					

NOTES
_____
_____
_____
_____

HOW THE DAY WENT? ☐ BAD   ☐ OK   ☐ GOOD   ☐ GREAT

DATE | | | S M T W T F S

WEIGHT POUNDS/KILOS **SLEEP** HOURS **WATER** OZ/ml

HOW I FEEL 😄 🙂 😐 ☹️   **ENERGY** 🔋 ▭▭▭▭▭ 🔋   **ACTIVITY** 🛏️ ▭▭▭▭ 🏃

☐ SUGAR FREE   ☐ ALCOHOL FREE   ☐ GLUTEN FREE   ☐ DAIRY FREE   ☐ LOW CARB   ☐ LOTS OF VEGGIES
☐ ORGANIC   ☐ NO PROCESSED FOODS

BREAKFAST TIME:	SERVING SIZE	PROTEIN	FAT	CARBS	CALORIES
SUBTOTAL					

LUNCH TIME:					
SUBTOTAL					

DINNER TIME:					
SUBTOTAL					

SNACKS TIME: / / /					
TOTAL					
vs. TARGET					

NOTES

_____

_____

_____

_____

HOW THE DAY WENT? BAD   OK   GOOD   GREAT

DATE | | | ☐☐☐☐☐☐☐ | **WEIGHT** | **SLEEP** | **WATER**
S M T W T F S | POUNDS/KILOS | HOURS | OZ/ml

HOW I FEEL ☺ ☺ ☺ ☹   ENERGY ▯▭▭▭▭▭▭ ▮   ACTIVITY 🛏▭▭▭▭▭ 🏃

☐ SUGAR FREE ☐ ALCOHOL FREE ☐ GLUTEN FREE ☐ DAIRY FREE ☐ LOW CARB ☐ LOTS OF VEGGIES
☐ ORGANIC ☐ NO PROCESSED FOODS

BREAKFAST TIME:	SERVING SIZE	PROTEIN	FAT	CARBS	CALORIES
SUBTOTAL					

LUNCH TIME:					
SUBTOTAL					

DINNER TIME:					
SUBTOTAL					

SNACKS TIME: / / /					
TOTAL					
vs. TARGET					

NOTES
_____
_____
_____
_____

HOW THE DAY WENT? ☐ BAD ☐ OK ☐ GOOD ☐ GREAT

DATE | | |

S M T W T F S

WEIGHT 🔲
POUNDS/KILOS

SLEEP 💤
HOURS

WATER 💧
OZ/ml

HOW I FEEL 😄 🙂 😐 ☹️   **ENERGY** 🔋⊏▭▭▭▭⊐🔋   **ACTIVITY** 🛏⊏▭▭▭▭⊐🏃

☐ SUGAR FREE   ☐ ALCOHOL FREE   ☐ GLUTEN FREE   ☐ DAIRY FREE   ☐ LOW CARB   ☐ LOTS OF VEGGIES

☐ ORGANIC   ☐ NO PROCESSED FOODS

BREAKFAST TIME:	SERVING SIZE	PROTEIN	FAT	CARBS	CALORIES
SUBTOTAL					

LUNCH TIME:					
SUBTOTAL					

DINNER TIME:					
SUBTOTAL					

SNACKS TIME: / / /					
TOTAL					
vs. TARGET					

NOTES

_____

_____

_____

_____

HOW THE DAY WENT? ☐ BAD ☐ OK ☐ GOOD ☐ GREAT

DATE | | | | | | | | | **WEIGHT**   **SLEEP**   **WATER**

S M T W T F S   POUNDS/KILOS   HOURS   OZ/ml

HOW I FEEL ☺ ☺ ☺ ☹   **ENERGY** ▯⊏⊓⊓⊓⊐🔋   **ACTIVITY** 🛏⊏⊓⊓⊐🏃

| ☐ SUGAR FREE | ☐ ALCOHOL FREE | ☐ GLUTEN FREE | ☐ DAIRY FREE | ☐ LOW CARB | ☐ LOTS OF VEGGIES |
| ☐ ORGANIC | ☐ NO PROCESSED FOODS | | | | |

BREAKFAST TIME:	SERVING SIZE	PROTEIN	FAT	CARBS	CALORIES
SUBTOTAL					
LUNCH TIME:					
SUBTOTAL					
DINNER TIME:					
SUBTOTAL					
SNACKS TIME: / / /					
TOTAL					
vs. TARGET					

NOTES

_____

_____

_____

_____

HOW THE DAY WENT? ☐ BAD ☐ OK ☐ GOOD ☐ GREAT

DATE | |

S M T W T F S

WEIGHT
POUNDS/KILOS

SLEEP
HOURS

WATER
OZ/ml

HOW I FEEL 😄 🙂 😐 ☹️ **ENERGY** 🔋▭▭▭▭🔋 **ACTIVITY** 🛏️▭▭▭▭🏃

☐ SUGAR FREE ☐ ALCOHOL FREE ☐ GLUTEN FREE ☐ DAIRY FREE ☐ LOW CARB ☐ LOTS OF VEGGIES
☐ ORGANIC ☐ NO PROCESSED FOODS

BREAKFAST TIME:	SERVING SIZE	PROTEIN	FAT	CARBS	CALORIES
SUBTOTAL					
LUNCH TIME:					
SUBTOTAL					
DINNER TIME:					
SUBTOTAL					
SNACKS TIME: / / /					
TOTAL					
vs. TARGET					

NOTES

_____

_____

_____

HOW THE DAY WENT? ☐ BAD ☐ OK ☐ GOOD ☐ GREAT

DATE | | | S M T W T F S | **WEIGHT** POUNDS/KILOS | **SLEEP** HOURS | **WATER** OZ/ml

HOW I FEEL 😀 ☺ 😐 ☹ **ENERGY** 🔋 ▭▭▭▭ 🔋 **ACTIVITY** 🛏 ▭▭▭▭ 🏃

☐ SUGAR FREE ☐ ALCOHOL FREE ☐ GLUTEN FREE ☐ DAIRY FREE ☐ LOW CARB ☐ LOTS OF VEGGIES
☐ ORGANIC ☐ NO PROCESSED FOODS

BREAKFAST TIME:	SERVING SIZE	PROTEIN	FAT	CARBS	CALORIES
SUBTOTAL					

LUNCH TIME:					
SUBTOTAL					

DINNER TIME:					
SUBTOTAL					

SNACKS TIME: / / /					
TOTAL					
vs. TARGET					

NOTES

_____

_____
_____
_____
_____

HOW THE DAY WENT? [BAD] [OK] [GOOD] [GREAT]

| DATE | | | | S M T W T F S | | WEIGHT POUNDS/KILOS | SLEEP HOURS | WATER OZ/ml |

HOW I FEEL 😄 🙂 😐 🙁   **ENERGY** 🔋 ▢▢▢▢ 🔋   **ACTIVITY** 🛏 ▢▢▢▢ 🏃

☐ SUGAR FREE   ☐ ALCOHOL FREE   ☐ GLUTEN FREE   ☐ DAIRY FREE   ☐ LOW CARB   ☐ LOTS OF VEGGIES
☐ ORGANIC   ☐ NO PROCESSED FOODS

BREAKFAST TIME:	SERVING SIZE	PROTEIN	FAT	CARBS	CALORIES
SUBTOTAL					

LUNCH TIME:					
SUBTOTAL					

DINNER TIME:					
SUBTOTAL					

SNACKS TIME: / / /					
TOTAL					
vs. TARGET					

NOTES
_____
_____
_____
_____

HOW THE DAY WENT? ☐ BAD   ☐ OK   ☐ GOOD   ☐ GREAT

DATE | | | ☐☐☐☐☐☐☐
S M T W T F S

WEIGHT | **SLEEP** | **WATER**
POUNDS/KILOS | HOURS | OZ/ml

HOW I FEEL 😃 🙂 😐 🙁   **ENERGY** ▭⊏⊏⊏⊏⊐▮   **ACTIVITY** 🛏⊏⊏⊏⊐🏃

☐ SUGAR FREE   ☐ ALCOHOL FREE   ☐ GLUTEN FREE   ☐ DAIRY FREE   ☐ LOW CARB   ☐ LOTS OF VEGGIES
☐ ORGANIC   ☐ NO PROCESSED FOODS

BREAKFAST TIME:	SERVING SIZE	PROTEIN	FAT	CARBS	CALORIES
SUBTOTAL					
LUNCH TIME:					
SUBTOTAL					
DINNER TIME:					
SUBTOTAL					
SNACKS TIME: / / /					
TOTAL					
vs. TARGET					

NOTES
_____
_____
_____
_____

HOW THE DAY WENT? ☐ BAD ☐ OK ☐ GOOD ☐ GREAT

DATE | | **WEIGHT**   **SLEEP**   **WATER**

S M T W T F S   POUNDS/KILOS   HOURS   OZ/ml

HOW I FEEL ☺ ☺ ☺ ☹   **ENERGY** 🔋 ▭▭▭▭▭ 🔋   **ACTIVITY** 🛏 ▭▭▭▭▭ 🏃

- [ ] SUGAR FREE
- [ ] ALCOHOL FREE
- [ ] GLUTEN FREE
- [ ] DAIRY FREE
- [ ] LOW CARB
- [ ] LOTS OF VEGGIES
- [ ] ORGANIC
- [ ] NO PROCESSED FOODS

BREAKFAST TIME:	SERVING SIZE	PROTEIN	FAT	CARBS	CALORIES
SUBTOTAL					
LUNCH TIME:					
SUBTOTAL					
DINNER TIME:					
SUBTOTAL					
SNACKS TIME: / / /					
TOTAL					
vs. TARGET					

NOTES

_____

_____

_____

_____

HOW THE DAY WENT? BAD   OK   GOOD   GREAT

DATE | | |

☐☐☐☐☐☐☐
S M T W T F S

WEIGHT
POUNDS/KILOS

SLEEP
HOURS

WATER
OZ/ml

HOW I FEEL ☺ ☺ ☺ ☹   **ENERGY** 🔋▭▭▭▭🔋   **ACTIVITY** 🛏▭▭▭▭🏃

☐ SUGAR FREE   ☐ ALCOHOL FREE   ☐ GLUTEN FREE   ☐ DAIRY FREE   ☐ LOW CARB   ☐ LOTS OF VEGGIES

☐ ORGANIC   ☐ NO PROCESSED FOODS

BREAKFAST TIME:	SERVING SIZE	PROTEIN	FAT	CARBS	CALORIES
SUBTOTAL					
LUNCH TIME:					
SUBTOTAL					
DINNER TIME:					
SUBTOTAL					
SNACKS TIME: / / /					
TOTAL					
vs. TARGET					

NOTES

_____

_____

_____

_____

HOW THE DAY WENT? ☐ BAD   ☐ OK   ☐ GOOD   ☐ GREAT

DATE | |

WEIGHT
POUNDS/KILOS

SLEEP
HOURS

WATER
OZ/ml

S M T W T F S

HOW I FEEL ☺ ☺ ☺ ☹   **ENERGY** ▯▭▭▭▭▭ ▮   **ACTIVITY** ⌫▭▭▭▭▭ 🏃

☐ SUGAR FREE ☐ ALCOHOL FREE ☐ GLUTEN FREE ☐ DAIRY FREE ☐ LOW CARB ☐ LOTS OF VEGGIES

☐ ORGANIC ☐ NO PROCESSED FOODS

BREAKFAST TIME:	SERVING SIZE	PROTEIN	FAT	CARBS	CALORIES
SUBTOTAL					
LUNCH TIME:					
SUBTOTAL					
DINNER TIME:					
SUBTOTAL					
SNACKS TIME: / / /					
TOTAL					
vs. TARGET					

NOTES

_____

_____

_____

HOW THE DAY WENT? ☐ BAD ☐ OK ☐ GOOD ☐ GREAT

DATE | | | ☐☐☐☐☐☐☐
S M T W T F S

WEIGHT
POUNDS/KILOS

SLEEP
HOURS

WATER
OZ/ml

HOW I FEEL 😣 🙂 😐 ☹   ENERGY 🔋 ⊂▭▭▭▭⊃ 🔋   ACTIVITY 🛏 ⊂▭▭▭▭⊃ 🏃

☐ SUGAR FREE   ☐ ALCOHOL FREE   ☐ GLUTEN FREE   ☐ DAIRY FREE   ☐ LOW CARB   ☐ LOTS OF VEGGIES
☐ ORGANIC   ☐ NO PROCESSED FOODS

BREAKFAST TIME:	SERVING SIZE	PROTEIN	FAT	CARBS	CALORIES
SUBTOTAL					
LUNCH TIME:					
SUBTOTAL					
DINNER TIME:					
SUBTOTAL					
SNACKS TIME: / / /					
TOTAL					
vs. TARGET					

NOTES
_____
_____
_____
_____

HOW THE DAY WENT? ☐ BAD ☐ OK ☐ GOOD ☐ GREAT

DATE | |

S M T W T F S

WEIGHT
POUNDS/KILOS

SLEEP
HOURS

WATER
OZ/ml

HOW I FEEL 😄 🙂 😐 ☹️   **ENERGY** 🔋 ▭▭▭▭ 🔋   **ACTIVITY** 🛏️ ▭▭▭▭ 🏃

☐ SUGAR FREE ☐ ALCOHOL FREE ☐ GLUTEN FREE ☐ DAIRY FREE ☐ LOW CARB ☐ LOTS OF VEGGIES

☐ ORGANIC ☐ NO PROCESSED FOODS

BREAKFAST TIME:	SERVING SIZE	PROTEIN	FAT	CARBS	CALORIES
SUBTOTAL					

LUNCH TIME:					
SUBTOTAL					

DINNER TIME:					
SUBTOTAL					

SNACKS TIME: / / /					
TOTAL					
vs. TARGET					

NOTES

_____

_____

_____

HOW THE DAY WENT? ☐ BAD ☐ OK ☐ GOOD ☐ GREAT

DATE | |

☐☐☐☐☐☐☐
S M T W T F S

WEIGHT
POUNDS/KILOS

SLEEP
HOURS

WATER
OZ/ml

HOW I FEEL 😄 🙂 😐 ☹️   **ENERGY** 🔋⊂▭▭▭▭▭▭⊃🔋   **ACTIVITY** 🛏⊂▭▭▭▭⊃🏃

☐ SUGAR FREE ☐ ALCOHOL FREE ☐ GLUTEN FREE ☐ DAIRY FREE ☐ LOW CARB ☐ LOTS OF VEGGIES
☐ ORGANIC ☐ NO PROCESSED FOODS

BREAKFAST TIME:	SERVING SIZE	PROTEIN	FAT	CARBS	CALORIES
SUBTOTAL					

LUNCH TIME:					
SUBTOTAL					

DINNER TIME:					
SUBTOTAL					

SNACKS TIME: / / /					
TOTAL					
vs. TARGET					

NOTES

_____

_____

_____

_____

HOW THE DAY WENT? ☐ BAD ☐ OK ☐ GOOD ☐ GREAT

DATE | | | □□□□□□ | **WEIGHT** | **SLEEP** | **WATER**
S M T W T F S | POUNDS/KILOS | HOURS | OZ/ml

HOW I FEEL 😆 🙂 😐 🙁 **ENERGY** 🔋 ▭▭▭▭ 🔋 **ACTIVITY** 🛏️ ▭▭▭▭ 🏃

☐ SUGAR FREE ☐ ALCOHOL FREE ☐ GLUTEN FREE ☐ DAIRY FREE ☐ LOW CARB ☐ LOTS OF VEGGIES

☐ ORGANIC ☐ NO PROCESSED FOODS

BREAKFAST TIME:	SERVING SIZE	PROTEIN	FAT	CARBS	CALORIES
SUBTOTAL					

LUNCH TIME:					
SUBTOTAL					

DINNER TIME:					
SUBTOTAL					

SNACKS TIME: / / /					
TOTAL					
vs. TARGET					

NOTES
_____
_____
_____
_____

HOW THE DAY WENT? ☐ BAD ☐ OK ☐ GOOD ☐ GREAT

DATE | | ☐☐☐☐☐☐☐   WEIGHT   SLEEP   WATER
S M T W T F S   POUNDS/KILOS   HOURS   OZ/ml

HOW I FEEL 😀 🙂 😐 🙁   ENERGY 🔋⊏▭▭▭▭⊐🔋   ACTIVITY 🛏⊏▭▭▭⊐🏃

☐ SUGAR FREE   ☐ ALCOHOL FREE   ☐ GLUTEN FREE   ☐ DAIRY FREE   ☐ LOW CARB   ☐ LOTS OF VEGGIES
☐ ORGANIC   ☐ NO PROCESSED FOODS

BREAKFAST TIME:	SERVING SIZE	PROTEIN	FAT	CARBS	CALORIES
SUBTOTAL					

LUNCH TIME:					
SUBTOTAL					

DINNER TIME:					
SUBTOTAL					

SNACKS TIME: / / /					
TOTAL					
vs. TARGET					

NOTES
_____
_____
_____
_____

HOW THE DAY WENT? ☐ BAD ☐ OK ☐ GOOD ☐ GREAT

DATE | |

S M T W T F S

WEIGHT POUNDS/KILOS

SLEEP HOURS

WATER OZ/ml

HOW I FEEL ☺ ☺ ☺ ☹   **ENERGY** 🔋 ▭▭▭▭ 🔋   **ACTIVITY** 🛏 ▭▭▭▭ 🏃

☐ SUGAR FREE ☐ ALCOHOL FREE ☐ GLUTEN FREE ☐ DAIRY FREE ☐ LOW CARB ☐ LOTS OF VEGGIES

☐ ORGANIC ☐ NO PROCESSED FOODS

BREAKFAST TIME:	SERVING SIZE	PROTEIN	FAT	CARBS	CALORIES
SUBTOTAL					
LUNCH TIME:					
SUBTOTAL					
DINNER TIME:					
SUBTOTAL					
SNACKS TIME: / / /					
TOTAL					
vs. TARGET					

NOTES

_____

_____

_____

HOW THE DAY WENT? ☐ BAD ☐ OK ☐ GOOD ☐ GREAT

DATE | | |

S M T W T F S

WEIGHT POUNDS/KILOS

SLEEP HOURS

WATER OZ/ml

HOW I FEEL ☺ ☺ ☺ ☹   **ENERGY** 🔋▭▭▭▭▭🔋   **ACTIVITY** 🛏▭▭▭▭🏃

- [ ] SUGAR FREE
- [ ] ALCOHOL FREE
- [ ] GLUTEN FREE
- [ ] DAIRY FREE
- [ ] LOW CARB
- [ ] LOTS OF VEGGIES
- [ ] ORGANIC
- [ ] NO PROCESSED FOODS

BREAKFAST TIME:	SERVING SIZE	PROTEIN	FAT	CARBS	CALORIES
SUBTOTAL					

LUNCH TIME:					
SUBTOTAL					

DINNER TIME:					
SUBTOTAL					

SNACKS TIME: / / /					
TOTAL					
vs. TARGET					

NOTES

_____

_____

_____

_____

HOW THE DAY WENT? [BAD] [OK] [GOOD] [GREAT]

DATE | | | ☐☐☐☐☐☐☐
S M T W T F S

WEIGHT
POUNDS/KILOS

SLEEP
HOURS

WATER
OZ/ml

HOW I FEEL 😄 🙂 😐 🙁 **ENERGY** ▯◁▭▭▭▭▷🔋 **ACTIVITY** 🛏◁▭▭▭▭▷🏃

☐ SUGAR FREE ☐ ALCOHOL FREE ☐ GLUTEN FREE ☐ DAIRY FREE ☐ LOW CARB ☐ LOTS OF VEGGIES
☐ ORGANIC ☐ NO PROCESSED FOODS

BREAKFAST TIME:	SERVING SIZE	PROTEIN	FAT	CARBS	CALORIES
SUBTOTAL					

LUNCH TIME:					
SUBTOTAL					

DINNER TIME:					
SUBTOTAL					

SNACKS TIME: / / /					
TOTAL					
vs. TARGET					

NOTES

_____

_____

_____

_____

HOW THE DAY WENT? ☐ BAD ☐ OK ☐ GOOD ☐ GREAT

DATE | |

S M T W T F S

WEIGHT
POUNDS/KILOS

SLEEP
HOURS

WATER
OZ/ml

HOW I FEEL ☺ ☺ ☺ ☹   **ENERGY** 🔋⊂▭▭▭⊃🔋   **ACTIVITY** 🛏⊂▭▭▭⊃🏃

☐ SUGAR FREE ☐ ALCOHOL FREE ☐ GLUTEN FREE ☐ DAIRY FREE ☐ LOW CARB ☐ LOTS OF VEGGIES
☐ ORGANIC ☐ NO PROCESSED FOODS

BREAKFAST TIME:	SERVING SIZE	PROTEIN	FAT	CARBS	CALORIES
SUBTOTAL					
LUNCH TIME:					
SUBTOTAL					
DINNER TIME:					
SUBTOTAL					
SNACKS TIME: / / /					
TOTAL					
vs. TARGET					

NOTES

_____

_____

_____

_____

HOW THE DAY WENT? ☐ BAD ☐ OK ☐ GOOD ☐ GREAT

DATE | | ☐☐☐☐☐☐☐
S M T W T F S

WEIGHT
POUNDS/KILOS

SLEEP
HOURS

WATER
OZ/ml

HOW I FEEL ☺ ☺ ☺ ☹   **ENERGY** 🔋⊏▭▭▭⊐🔋   **ACTIVITY** 🛏⊏▭▭▭⊐🏃

☐ SUGAR FREE ☐ ALCOHOL FREE ☐ GLUTEN FREE ☐ DAIRY FREE ☐ LOW CARB ☐ LOTS OF VEGGIES

☐ ORGANIC ☐ NO PROCESSED FOODS

BREAKFAST TIME:	SERVING SIZE	PROTEIN	FAT	CARBS	CALORIES
SUBTOTAL					

LUNCH TIME:					
SUBTOTAL					

DINNER TIME:					
SUBTOTAL					

SNACKS TIME: / / /					
TOTAL					
vs. TARGET					

NOTES
_____
_____
_____
_____

HOW THE DAY WENT? ☐ BAD ☐ OK ☐ GOOD ☐ GREAT

DATE | | |

S M T W T F S

WEIGHT
POUNDS/KILOS

SLEEP
HOURS

WATER
OZ/ml

HOW I FEEL ☺ ☺ ☺ ☹   **ENERGY** ▯ ⊏▭▭▭▭▭⊐ 🔋   **ACTIVITY** 🛏 ⊏▭▭▭▭⊐ 🏃

☐ SUGAR FREE ☐ ALCOHOL FREE ☐ GLUTEN FREE ☐ DAIRY FREE ☐ LOW CARB ☐ LOTS OF VEGGIES

☐ ORGANIC ☐ NO PROCESSED FOODS

BREAKFAST TIME:	SERVING SIZE	PROTEIN	FAT	CARBS	CALORIES
SUBTOTAL					
LUNCH TIME:					
SUBTOTAL					
DINNER TIME:					
SUBTOTAL					
SNACKS TIME: / / /					
TOTAL					
vs. TARGET					

NOTES

_____

_____

_____

_____

HOW THE DAY WENT? ☐ BAD ☐ OK ☐ GOOD ☐ GREAT

DATE | | | □□□□□□□
S M T W T F S

WEIGHT
POUNDS/KILOS

SLEEP
HOURS

WATER
OZ/ml

HOW I FEEL ☺ ☺ ☺ ☹ **ENERGY** ▯ ⊏▭▭▭▭⊐ ▮ **ACTIVITY** 🛏 ⊏▭▭▭▭⊐ 🏃

☐ SUGAR FREE   ☐ ALCOHOL FREE   ☐ GLUTEN FREE   ☐ DAIRY FREE   ☐ LOW CARB   ☐ LOTS OF VEGGIES

☐ ORGANIC   ☐ NO PROCESSED FOODS

BREAKFAST TIME:	SERVING SIZE	PROTEIN	FAT	CARBS	CALORIES
SUBTOTAL					
LUNCH TIME:					
SUBTOTAL					
DINNER TIME:					
SUBTOTAL					
SNACKS TIME: / / /					
TOTAL					
vs. TARGET					

NOTES

_____

_____

_____

HOW THE DAY WENT? ☐ BAD ☐ OK ☐ GOOD ☐ GREAT

DATE | | | □ □ □ □ □ □ □
S M T W T F S

WEIGHT _____
POUNDS/KILOS

SLEEP _____
HOURS

WATER _____
OZ/ml

HOW I FEEL ☺ ☺ ☺ ☹   **ENERGY** 🔋 ▭▭▭▭ 🔋   **ACTIVITY** 🛏 ▭▭▭▭ 🏃

☐ SUGAR FREE   ☐ ALCOHOL FREE   ☐ GLUTEN FREE   ☐ DAIRY FREE   ☐ LOW CARB   ☐ LOTS OF VEGGIES
☐ ORGANIC   ☐ NO PROCESSED FOODS

BREAKFAST TIME:	SERVING SIZE	PROTEIN	FAT	CARBS	CALORIES
SUBTOTAL					

LUNCH TIME:					
SUBTOTAL					

DINNER TIME:					
SUBTOTAL					

SNACKS TIME: / / /					
TOTAL					
vs. TARGET					

NOTES
_____
_____
_____
_____

HOW THE DAY WENT? ☐ BAD ☐ OK ☐ GOOD ☐ GREAT

DATE				S M T W T F S	WEIGHT	SLEEP	WATER
					POUNDS/KILOS	HOURS	OZ/ml

HOW I FEEL ☺ ☺ ☺ ☹   ENERGY 🔋 ▭▭▭▭ 🔋   ACTIVITY 🛏 ▭▭▭▭ 🏃

☐ SUGAR FREE ☐ ALCOHOL FREE ☐ GLUTEN FREE ☐ DAIRY FREE ☐ LOW CARB ☐ LOTS OF VEGGIES
☐ ORGANIC ☐ NO PROCESSED FOODS

BREAKFAST TIME:	SERVING SIZE	PROTEIN	FAT	CARBS	CALORIES
SUBTOTAL					
LUNCH TIME:					
SUBTOTAL					
DINNER TIME:					
SUBTOTAL					
SNACKS TIME: / / /					
TOTAL					
vs. TARGET					

NOTES
_____
_____
_____
_____

HOW THE DAY WENT? ☐ BAD ☐ OK ☐ GOOD ☐ GREAT

DATE | | | □□□□□□□ **WEIGHT** **SLEEP** **WATER**
S M T W T F S

POUNDS/KILOS | HOURS | OZ/ml

HOW I FEEL ☺ ☺ ☺ ☹ **ENERGY** 🔋▭▭▭▭▭🔋 **ACTIVITY** 🛏▭▭▭▭ 🏃

☐ SUGAR FREE ☐ ALCOHOL FREE ☐ GLUTEN FREE ☐ DAIRY FREE ☐ LOW CARB ☐ LOTS OF VEGGIES

☐ ORGANIC ☐ NO PROCESSED FOODS

BREAKFAST TIME:	SERVING SIZE	PROTEIN	FAT	CARBS	CALORIES
SUBTOTAL					

LUNCH TIME:					
SUBTOTAL					

DINNER TIME:					
SUBTOTAL					

SNACKS TIME: / / /					
TOTAL					
vs. TARGET					

NOTES

_____

_____

_____

_____

HOW THE DAY WENT? ☐ BAD ☐ OK ☐ GOOD ☐ GREAT

DATE | | | ☐☐☐☐☐☐☐ **WEIGHT** **SLEEP** **WATER**
S M T W T F S | POUNDS/KILOS | HOURS | OZ/ml

HOW I FEEL 😃 🙂 😐 ☹ **ENERGY** 🔋⊂▭▭▭▭⊃🔋 **ACTIVITY** 🛏⊂▭▭▭▭⊃🏃

☐ SUGAR FREE ☐ ALCOHOL FREE ☐ GLUTEN FREE ☐ DAIRY FREE ☐ LOW CARB ☐ LOTS OF VEGGIES
☐ ORGANIC ☐ NO PROCESSED FOODS

BREAKFAST TIME:	SERVING SIZE	PROTEIN	FAT	CARBS	CALORIES
SUBTOTAL					

LUNCH TIME:					
SUBTOTAL					

DINNER TIME:					
SUBTOTAL					

SNACKS TIME: / / /					
TOTAL					
vs. TARGET					

NOTES
_____
_____
_____
_____

HOW THE DAY WENT? ☐ BAD ☐ OK ☐ GOOD ☐ GREAT

DATE | | | S M T W T F S   **WEIGHT** _____ POUNDS/KILOS   **SLEEP** _____ HOURS   **WATER** _____ OZ/ml

HOW I FEEL ☺ ☺ ☹ ☹   **ENERGY** ▯▭▭▭▭▭▭▮   **ACTIVITY** ▭▭▭▭▭▭

☐ SUGAR FREE   ☐ ALCOHOL FREE   ☐ GLUTEN FREE   ☐ DAIRY FREE   ☐ LOW CARB   ☐ LOTS OF VEGGIES
☐ ORGANIC   ☐ NO PROCESSED FOODS

BREAKFAST TIME:	SERVING SIZE	PROTEIN	FAT	CARBS	CALORIES
SUBTOTAL					

LUNCH TIME:					
SUBTOTAL					

DINNER TIME:					
SUBTOTAL					

SNACKS TIME: / / /					
TOTAL					
vs. TARGET					

NOTES
_____
_____
_____
_____

HOW THE DAY WENT? ☐ BAD ☐ OK ☐ GOOD ☐ GREAT

DATE | | | | □□□□□□□ | WEIGHT | SLEEP | WATER
S M T W T F S | POUNDS/KILOS | HOURS | OZ/ml

HOW I FEEL 😄 😊 😐 ☹️ ENERGY 🔋⊂━━━━⊃🔋 ACTIVITY 🛏️⊂━━━⊃🏃

☐ SUGAR FREE ☐ ALCOHOL FREE ☐ GLUTEN FREE ☐ DAIRY FREE ☐ LOW CARB ☐ LOTS OF VEGGIES
☐ ORGANIC ☐ NO PROCESSED FOODS

BREAKFAST TIME:	SERVING SIZE	PROTEIN	FAT	CARBS	CALORIES
SUBTOTAL					

LUNCH TIME:					
SUBTOTAL					

DINNER TIME:					
SUBTOTAL					

SNACKS TIME: / / /					
TOTAL					
vs. TARGET					

NOTES
_____
_____
_____
_____

HOW THE DAY WENT? ☐ BAD ☐ OK ☐ GOOD ☐ GREAT

DATE | | | ☐☐☐☐☐☐☐   **WEIGHT**   **SLEEP**   **WATER**

S M T W T F S   POUNDS/KILOS   HOURS   OZ/ml

HOW I FEEL ☺ ☺ ☺ ☹   **ENERGY** 🔋 ⊂▭▭▭▭⊃ 🔋   **ACTIVITY** 🛏 ⊂▭▭▭⊃ 🏃

☐ SUGAR FREE   ☐ ALCOHOL FREE   ☐ GLUTEN FREE   ☐ DAIRY FREE   ☐ LOW CARB   ☐ LOTS OF VEGGIES

☐ ORGANIC   ☐ NO PROCESSED FOODS

BREAKFAST TIME:	SERVING SIZE	PROTEIN	FAT	CARBS	CALORIES
SUBTOTAL					
LUNCH TIME:					
SUBTOTAL					
DINNER TIME:					
SUBTOTAL					
SNACKS TIME: / / /					
TOTAL					
vs. TARGET					

NOTES

_____

_____

_____

_____

HOW THE DAY WENT? ☐ BAD ☐ OK ☐ GOOD ☐ GREAT

DATE | | | ⬜⬜⬜⬜⬜⬜⬜
S M T W T F S

WEIGHT
POUNDS/KILOS

SLEEP
HOURS

WATER
OZ/ml

HOW I FEEL 😁 🙂 😐 😟   ENERGY ▯⊏⊏⊏⊏⊏⊃🔋   ACTIVITY 🛏⊏⊏⊏⊏⊃🏃

☐ SUGAR FREE   ☐ ALCOHOL FREE   ☐ GLUTEN FREE   ☐ DAIRY FREE   ☐ LOW CARB   ☐ LOTS OF VEGGIES

☐ ORGANIC   ☐ NO PROCESSED FOODS

BREAKFAST TIME:	SERVING SIZE	PROTEIN	FAT	CARBS	CALORIES
SUBTOTAL					

LUNCH TIME:					
SUBTOTAL					

DINNER TIME:					
SUBTOTAL					

SNACKS TIME: / / /					
TOTAL					
vs. TARGET					

NOTES

_____

_____

_____

_____

HOW THE DAY WENT? ☐ BAD ☐ OK ☐ GOOD ☐ GREAT

DATE | | |

S M T W T F S

WEIGHT
POUNDS/KILOS

SLEEP
HOURS

WATER
OZ/ml

HOW I FEEL 😄 🙂 😐 🙁   ENERGY 🔋 ⊏▭▭▭▭▭⊐ 🔋   ACTIVITY 🛏 ⊏▭▭▭▭⊐ 🏃

| SUGAR FREE | ALCOHOL FREE | GLUTEN FREE | DAIRY FREE | LOW CARB | LOTS OF VEGGIES |
| ORGANIC | NO PROCESSED FOODS | | | | |

BREAKFAST TIME:	SERVING SIZE	PROTEIN	FAT	CARBS	CALORIES
SUBTOTAL					

LUNCH TIME:					
SUBTOTAL					

DINNER TIME:					
SUBTOTAL					

SNACKS TIME: / / /					
TOTAL					
vs. TARGET					

NOTES
_____
_____
_____
_____

HOW THE DAY WENT? | BAD | OK | GOOD | GREAT |

DATE | | | ⬜⬜⬜⬜⬜⬜ **WEIGHT** **SLEEP** **WATER**
S M T W T F S   POUNDS/KILOS   HOURS   OZ/ml

HOW I FEEL 😃 🙂 😐 ☹️   ENERGY ▯▭▭▭▭🔋   ACTIVITY 🛏▭▭▭▭🏃

⬜ SUGAR FREE ⬜ ALCOHOL FREE ⬜ GLUTEN FREE ⬜ DAIRY FREE ⬜ LOW CARB ⬜ LOTS OF VEGGIES
⬜ ORGANIC ⬜ NO PROCESSED FOODS

BREAKFAST TIME:	SERVING SIZE	PROTEIN	FAT	CARBS	CALORIES
SUBTOTAL					

LUNCH TIME:					
SUBTOTAL					

DINNER TIME:					
SUBTOTAL					

SNACKS TIME: / / /					
TOTAL					
vs. TARGET					

NOTES
_____
_____
_____
_____

HOW THE DAY WENT? [BAD] [OK] [GOOD] [GREAT]

DATE | | _____ ☐☐☐☐☐☐☐ **WEIGHT** ⚖ _____ **SLEEP** 😴 _____ **WATER** 💧 _____
S M T W T F S   POUNDS/KILOS   HOURS   OZ/ml

HOW I FEEL 😄 🙂 😐 ☹ **ENERGY** 🔋⊏⊏⊏⊏⊐🔋 **ACTIVITY** 🛏⊏⊏⊏⊐🏃

☐ SUGAR FREE ☐ ALCOHOL FREE ☐ GLUTEN FREE ☐ DAIRY FREE ☐ LOW CARB ☐ LOTS OF VEGGIES
☐ ORGANIC ☐ NO PROCESSED FOODS

BREAKFAST TIME:	SERVING SIZE	PROTEIN	FAT	CARBS	CALORIES
SUBTOTAL					

LUNCH TIME:					
SUBTOTAL					

DINNER TIME:					
SUBTOTAL					

SNACKS TIME: / / /					
TOTAL					
vs. TARGET					

NOTES
_____
_____
_____
_____

HOW THE DAY WENT? ☐ BAD ☐ OK ☐ GOOD ☐ GREAT

DATE | |

S M T W T F S

WEIGHT
POUNDS/KILOS

SLEEP
HOURS

WATER
OZ/ml

HOW I FEEL ☺ ☺ ☺ ☹ **ENERGY** 🔋 ▭▭▭▭ 🔋 **ACTIVITY** 🛏 ▭▭▭▭ 🏃

☐ SUGAR FREE ☐ ALCOHOL FREE ☐ GLUTEN FREE ☐ DAIRY FREE ☐ LOW CARB ☐ LOTS OF VEGGIES
☐ ORGANIC ☐ NO PROCESSED FOODS

BREAKFAST TIME:	SERVING SIZE	PROTEIN	FAT	CARBS	CALORIES
SUBTOTAL					
LUNCH TIME:					
SUBTOTAL					
DINNER TIME:					
SUBTOTAL					
SNACKS TIME: / / /					
TOTAL					
vs. TARGET					

NOTES

_____

_____

_____

_____

HOW THE DAY WENT? ☐ BAD ☐ OK ☐ GOOD ☐ GREAT

DATE | |

S M T W T F S

| | ☺ | | |

WEIGHT
POUNDS/KILOS

SLEEP
HOURS

WATER
OZ/ml

HOW I FEEL ☺ ☺ ☺ ☹   **ENERGY** 🔋 ⊂▭▭▭▭⊃ 🔋   **ACTIVITY** 🛏 ⊂▭▭▭⊃ 🏃

| ☐ SUGAR FREE | ☐ ALCOHOL FREE | ☐ GLUTEN FREE | ☐ DAIRY FREE | ☐ LOW CARB | ☐ LOTS OF VEGGIES |
| ☐ ORGANIC | ☐ NO PROCESSED FOODS |

BREAKFAST TIME:	SERVING SIZE	PROTEIN	FAT	CARBS	CALORIES
SUBTOTAL					

LUNCH TIME:					
SUBTOTAL					

DINNER TIME:					
SUBTOTAL					

SNACKS TIME: / / /					
TOTAL					
vs. TARGET					

NOTES

_____

_____

_____

_____

HOW THE DAY WENT? ☐ BAD ☐ OK ☐ GOOD ☐ GREAT

DATE | | | ☐☐☐☐☐☐☐
S M T W T F S

WEIGHT
POUNDS/KILOS

SLEEP
HOURS

WATER
OZ/ml

HOW I FEEL ☺ ☺ ☺ ☹   **ENERGY** ▯⊂☐☐☐☐▮   **ACTIVITY** 🛏⊂☐☐☐☐ 🏃

☐ SUGAR FREE   ☐ ALCOHOL FREE   ☐ GLUTEN FREE   ☐ DAIRY FREE   ☐ LOW CARB   ☐ LOTS OF VEGGIES

☐ ORGANIC   ☐ NO PROCESSED FOODS

BREAKFAST TIME:	SERVING SIZE	PROTEIN	FAT	CARBS	CALORIES
SUBTOTAL					
LUNCH TIME:					
SUBTOTAL					
DINNER TIME:					
SUBTOTAL					
SNACKS TIME: / / /					
TOTAL					
vs. TARGET					

NOTES
_____
_____
_____
_____

HOW THE DAY WENT? ☐ BAD ☐ OK ☐ GOOD ☐ GREAT

DATE | | | S M T W T F S

WEIGHT
POUNDS/KILOS

SLEEP
HOURS

WATER
OZ/ml

HOW I FEEL ☺ ☺ ☺ ☹   ENERGY ▯⊂▭▭▭▭▭▭▭▯ 🔋   ACTIVITY 🛏 ⊂▭▭▭▭▭▯ 🏃

| | SUGAR FREE | | ALCOHOL FREE | | GLUTEN FREE | | DAIRY FREE | | LOW CARB | | LOTS OF VEGGIES |

| | ORGANIC | | NO PROCESSED FOODS |

BREAKFAST TIME:	SERVING SIZE	PROTEIN	FAT	CARBS	CALORIES
SUBTOTAL					

LUNCH TIME:					
SUBTOTAL					

DINNER TIME:					
SUBTOTAL					

SNACKS TIME: / / /					
TOTAL					
VS. TARGET					

NOTES

HOW THE DAY WENT? | BAD | OK | GOOD | GREAT |

DATE | | | ☐☐☐☐☐☐☐

S M T W T F S

WEIGHT

POUNDS/KILOS

SLEEP

HOURS

WATER

OZ/ml

HOW I FEEL ☺ ☺ ☹ ☹   **ENERGY** ▯ ⟨▭▭▭▭⟩ ▮   **ACTIVITY** ⍐ ⟨▭▭▭▭⟩ 🏃

☐ SUGAR FREE   ☐ ALCOHOL FREE   ☐ GLUTEN FREE   ☐ DAIRY FREE   ☐ LOW CARB   ☐ LOTS OF VEGGIES

☐ ORGANIC   ☐ NO PROCESSED FOODS

BREAKFAST TIME:	SERVING SIZE	PROTEIN	FAT	CARBS	CALORIES
SUBTOTAL					
LUNCH TIME:					
SUBTOTAL					
DINNER TIME:					
SUBTOTAL					
SNACKS TIME: / / /					
TOTAL					
vs. TARGET					

NOTES

_____

_____

_____

_____

HOW THE DAY WENT? ☐ BAD ☐ OK ☐ GOOD ☐ GREAT

DATE | | | ☐☐☐☐☐☐☐
S M T W T F S

WEIGHT
POUNDS/KILOS

SLEEP
HOURS

WATER
OZ/ml

HOW I FEEL 😄 🙂 😐 ☹️   **ENERGY** 🔋⬜⬜⬜⬜🔋   **ACTIVITY** 🛏️⬜⬜⬜⬜ 🏃

☐ SUGAR FREE   ☐ ALCOHOL FREE   ☐ GLUTEN FREE   ☐ DAIRY FREE   ☐ LOW CARB   ☐ LOTS OF VEGGIES
☐ ORGANIC   ☐ NO PROCESSED FOODS

BREAKFAST TIME:	SERVING SIZE	PROTEIN	FAT	CARBS	CALORIES
SUBTOTAL					
LUNCH TIME:					
SUBTOTAL					
DINNER TIME:					
SUBTOTAL					
SNACKS TIME: / / /					
TOTAL					
vs. TARGET					

NOTES
_____
_____
_____
_____

HOW THE DAY WENT? ☐ BAD   ☐ OK   ☐ GOOD   ☐ GREAT

DATE | | | □ □ □ □ □ □ □
S M T W T F S

WEIGHT
POUNDS/KILOS

SLEEP
HOURS

WATER
OZ/ml

HOW I FEEL 😄 😊 😐 ☹️　**ENERGY** 🔋 ▭▭▭▭ 🔋　**ACTIVITY** 🛏️ ▭▭▭▭ 🏃

□ SUGAR FREE　　□ ALCOHOL FREE　　□ GLUTEN FREE　　□ DAIRY FREE　　□ LOW CARB　　□ LOTS OF VEGGIES

□ ORGANIC　　□ NO PROCESSED FOODS

BREAKFAST TIME:	SERVING SIZE	PROTEIN	FAT	CARBS	CALORIES
SUBTOTAL					

LUNCH TIME:					
SUBTOTAL					

DINNER TIME:					
SUBTOTAL					

SNACKS TIME: / / /					
TOTAL					
vs. TARGET					

NOTES

_____

_____

_____

_____

HOW THE DAY WENT? [BAD] [OK] [GOOD] [GREAT]

DATE | | | ☐☐☐☐☐☐☐
S M T W T F S

WEIGHT
POUNDS/KILOS

SLEEP
HOURS

WATER
OZ/ml

HOW I FEEL 😄 🙂 😐 ☹️   **ENERGY** 🔋 ▭▭▭▭▭ 🔋   **ACTIVITY** 🛏️ ▭▭▭▭▭ 🏃

☐ SUGAR FREE   ☐ ALCOHOL FREE   ☐ GLUTEN FREE   ☐ DAIRY FREE   ☐ LOW CARB   ☐ LOTS OF VEGGIES

☐ ORGANIC   ☐ NO PROCESSED FOODS

BREAKFAST TIME:	SERVING SIZE	PROTEIN	FAT	CARBS	CALORIES
SUBTOTAL					
LUNCH TIME:					
SUBTOTAL					
DINNER TIME:					
SUBTOTAL					
SNACKS TIME: / / /					
TOTAL					
vs. TARGET					

NOTES

_____

_____

_____

_____

HOW THE DAY WENT? ☐ BAD ☐ OK ☐ GOOD ☐ GREAT

DATE | | | S M T W T F S

WEIGHT POUNDS/KILOS **SLEEP** HOURS **WATER** OZ/ml

HOW I FEEL 😆 🙂 😐 🙁 **ENERGY** 🔋 ⊏⊐⊐⊐⊐ 🔋 **ACTIVITY** 🛏 ⊏⊐⊐⊐ 🏃

| | SUGAR FREE | | ALCOHOL FREE | | GLUTEN FREE | | DAIRY FREE | | LOW CARB | | LOTS OF VEGGIES |
| | ORGANIC | | NO PROCESSED FOODS |

BREAKFAST TIME:	SERVING SIZE	PROTEIN	FAT	CARBS	CALORIES
SUBTOTAL					

LUNCH TIME:					
SUBTOTAL					

DINNER TIME:					
SUBTOTAL					

SNACKS TIME: / / /					
TOTAL					
vs. TARGET					

NOTES

_____

_____

_____

_____

HOW THE DAY WENT? BAD OK GOOD GREAT

DATE | | | S M T W T F S   **WEIGHT** POUNDS/KILOS   **SLEEP** HOURS   **WATER** OZ/ml

HOW I FEEL 😄 🙂 😐 🙁   **ENERGY** 🔋⊏⊐▯   **ACTIVITY** 🛏⊏⊐🏃

☐ SUGAR FREE   ☐ ALCOHOL FREE   ☐ GLUTEN FREE   ☐ DAIRY FREE   ☐ LOW CARB   ☐ LOTS OF VEGGIES
☐ ORGANIC   ☐ NO PROCESSED FOODS

BREAKFAST TIME:	SERVING SIZE	PROTEIN	FAT	CARBS	CALORIES
SUBTOTAL					
LUNCH TIME:					
SUBTOTAL					
DINNER TIME:					
SUBTOTAL					
SNACKS TIME: / / /					
TOTAL					
vs. TARGET					

NOTES

HOW THE DAY WENT? ☐ BAD ☐ OK ☐ GOOD ☐ GREAT

DATE | | ☐☐☐☐☐☐☐   **WEIGHT**   **SLEEP**   **WATER**
S M T W T F S

POUNDS/KILOS   HOURS   OZ/ml

HOW I FEEL 😄 🙂 😐 ☹️   **ENERGY** 🔋 ⊂▭▭▭▭▭▭▭⊃ 🔋   **ACTIVITY** 🛏 ⊂▭▭▭▭⊃ 🏃

☐ SUGAR FREE ☐ ALCOHOL FREE ☐ GLUTEN FREE ☐ DAIRY FREE ☐ LOW CARB ☐ LOTS OF VEGGIES
☐ ORGANIC ☐ NO PROCESSED FOODS

BREAKFAST TIME:	SERVING SIZE	PROTEIN	FAT	CARBS	CALORIES
SUBTOTAL					

LUNCH TIME:					
SUBTOTAL					

DINNER TIME:					
SUBTOTAL					

SNACKS TIME: / / /					
TOTAL					
vs. TARGET					

NOTES

_____

_____

_____

_____

HOW THE DAY WENT? ☐ BAD ☐ OK ☐ GOOD ☐ GREAT

DATE | | | □ □ □ □ □ □ □
S M T W T F S

WEIGHT
POUNDS/KILOS

SLEEP
HOURS

WATER
OZ/ml

HOW I FEEL ☺ ☺ ☹ ☹ **ENERGY** 🔋 ⊂▭▭▭⊃ 🔋 **ACTIVITY** 🛏 ⊂▭▭▭⊃ 🏃

☐ SUGAR FREE   ☐ ALCOHOL FREE   ☐ GLUTEN FREE   ☐ DAIRY FREE   ☐ LOW CARB   ☐ LOTS OF VEGGIES
☐ ORGANIC   ☐ NO PROCESSED FOODS

BREAKFAST TIME:	SERVING SIZE	PROTEIN	FAT	CARBS	CALORIES
SUBTOTAL					

LUNCH TIME:					
SUBTOTAL					

DINNER TIME:					
SUBTOTAL					

SNACKS TIME: / / /					
TOTAL					
vs. TARGET					

NOTES

_____

_____

_____

HOW THE DAY WENT? ☐ BAD ☐ OK ☐ GOOD ☐ GREAT

DATE | | |

☐☐☐☐☐☐☐
S M T W T F S

WEIGHT
POUNDS/KILOS

SLEEP
HOURS

WATER
OZ/ml

HOW I FEEL ☺ ☺ ☹ ☹   **ENERGY** 🔋 ⊂▭▭▭▭▭▭⊃ 🔋   **ACTIVITY** 🛏 ⊂▭▭▭▭⊃ 🏃

☐ SUGAR FREE   ☐ ALCOHOL FREE   ☐ GLUTEN FREE   ☐ DAIRY FREE   ☐ LOW CARB   ☐ LOTS OF VEGGIES

☐ ORGANIC   ☐ NO PROCESSED FOODS

BREAKFAST TIME:	SERVING SIZE	PROTEIN	FAT	CARBS	CALORIES
SUBTOTAL					
LUNCH TIME:					
SUBTOTAL					
DINNER TIME:					
SUBTOTAL					
SNACKS TIME: / / /					
TOTAL					
vs. TARGET					

NOTES

_____

_____

_____

HOW THE DAY WENT? ☐ BAD   ☐ OK   ☐ GOOD   ☐ GREAT

DATE | | | ☐☐☐☐☐☐☐ ⚖ **WEIGHT**   🌙 **SLEEP**   💧 **WATER**

S M T W T F S | POUNDS/KILOS | HOURS | OZ/ml

HOW I FEEL 😄 🙂 😐 ☹   **ENERGY** 🔋 ⊏⊐⊐⊐⊐⊐ 🔋   **ACTIVITY** 🛏 ⊏⊐⊐⊐⊐ 🏃

| ☐ | SUGAR FREE | ☐ | ALCOHOL FREE | ☐ | GLUTEN FREE | ☐ | DAIRY FREE | ☐ | LOW CARB | ☐ | LOTS OF VEGGIES |

| ☐ | ORGANIC | ☐ | NO PROCESSED FOODS |

BREAKFAST TIME:	SERVING SIZE	PROTEIN	FAT	CARBS	CALORIES
SUBTOTAL					
LUNCH TIME:					
SUBTOTAL					
DINNER TIME:					
SUBTOTAL					
SNACKS TIME: / / /					
TOTAL					
vs. TARGET					

NOTES

_____

_____

_____

_____

HOW THE DAY WENT? ☐ BAD ☐ OK ☐ GOOD ☐ GREAT

DATE | |

S M T W T F S

WEIGHT
POUNDS/KILOS

SLEEP
HOURS

WATER
OZ/ml

HOW I FEEL ☺ ☺ ☹ ☹   **ENERGY** 🔋 ▭▭▭▭ 🔋   **ACTIVITY** 🛏 ▭▭▭▭ 🏃

☐ SUGAR FREE   ☐ ALCOHOL FREE   ☐ GLUTEN FREE   ☐ DAIRY FREE   ☐ LOW CARB   ☐ LOTS OF VEGGIES

☐ ORGANIC   ☐ NO PROCESSED FOODS

BREAKFAST TIME:	SERVING SIZE	PROTEIN	FAT	CARBS	CALORIES
SUBTOTAL					
LUNCH TIME:					
SUBTOTAL					
DINNER TIME:					
SUBTOTAL					
SNACKS TIME: / / /					
TOTAL					
vs. TARGET					

NOTES

_____

_____

_____

HOW THE DAY WENT? ☐ BAD ☐ OK ☐ GOOD ☐ GREAT

DATE | | | ☐☐☐☐☐☐☐
S M T W T F S

WEIGHT
POUNDS/KILOS

SLEEP
HOURS

WATER
OZ/ml

HOW I FEEL 😃 🙂 😐 ☹️   **ENERGY** 🔋 ⊂▭▭▭▭▭▭⊃ 🔋   **ACTIVITY** 🛏 ⊂▭▭▭▭⊃ 🏃

☐ SUGAR FREE   ☐ ALCOHOL FREE   ☐ GLUTEN FREE   ☐ DAIRY FREE   ☐ LOW CARB   ☐ LOTS OF VEGGIES

☐ ORGANIC   ☐ NO PROCESSED FOODS

BREAKFAST TIME:	SERVING SIZE	PROTEIN	FAT	CARBS	CALORIES
SUBTOTAL					
LUNCH TIME:					
SUBTOTAL					
DINNER TIME:					
SUBTOTAL					
SNACKS TIME: / / /					
TOTAL					
vs. TARGET					

NOTES

_____

_____

_____

_____

HOW THE DAY WENT? ☐ BAD   ☐ OK   ☐ GOOD   ☐ GREAT

DATE | |

S M T W T F S

WEIGHT
POUNDS/KILOS

SLEEP
HOURS

WATER
OZ/ml

HOW I FEEL ☺ ☺ ☺ ☹   **ENERGY** 🔋 ▭▭▭▭ 🔋   **ACTIVITY** 🛏 ▭▭▭▭ 🏃

☐ SUGAR FREE   ☐ ALCOHOL FREE   ☐ GLUTEN FREE   ☐ DAIRY FREE   ☐ LOW CARB   ☐ LOTS OF VEGGIES
☐ ORGANIC   ☐ NO PROCESSED FOODS

BREAKFAST TIME:	SERVING SIZE	PROTEIN	FAT	CARBS	CALORIES
SUBTOTAL					
LUNCH TIME:					
SUBTOTAL					
DINNER TIME:					
SUBTOTAL					
SNACKS TIME: / / /					
TOTAL					
vs. TARGET					

NOTES

_____

_____

_____

_____

HOW THE DAY WENT? ☐ BAD   ☐ OK   ☐ GOOD   ☐ GREAT

DATE | |

S M T W T F S

WEIGHT
POUNDS/KILOS

SLEEP
HOURS

WATER
OZ/ml

HOW I FEEL ☺ ☺ ☺ ☹   **ENERGY** ▭▭▭▭▭   **ACTIVITY** ▭▭▭▭▭

☐ SUGAR FREE ☐ ALCOHOL FREE ☐ GLUTEN FREE ☐ DAIRY FREE ☐ LOW CARB ☐ LOTS OF VEGGIES
☐ ORGANIC ☐ NO PROCESSED FOODS

BREAKFAST TIME:	SERVING SIZE	PROTEIN	FAT	CARBS	CALORIES
SUBTOTAL					
LUNCH TIME:					
SUBTOTAL					
DINNER TIME:					
SUBTOTAL					
SNACKS TIME: / / /					
TOTAL					
vs. TARGET					

NOTES

_____

_____

_____

HOW THE DAY WENT? ☐ BAD ☐ OK ☐ GOOD ☐ GREAT

DATE | | ☐☐☐☐☐☐☐ **WEIGHT** **SLEEP** **WATER**
S M T W T F S POUNDS/KILOS HOURS OZ/ml

HOW I FEEL 😀 🙂 😐 ☹️ **ENERGY** 🔋⊏⊐⊐⊐⊐🔋 **ACTIVITY** 🛏⊏⊐⊐⊐⊐ 🏃

☐ SUGAR FREE ☐ ALCOHOL FREE ☐ GLUTEN FREE ☐ DAIRY FREE ☐ LOW CARB ☐ LOTS OF VEGGIES

☐ ORGANIC ☐ NO PROCESSED FOODS

BREAKFAST TIME:	SERVING SIZE	PROTEIN	FAT	CARBS	CALORIES
SUBTOTAL					
LUNCH TIME:					
SUBTOTAL					
DINNER TIME:					
SUBTOTAL					
SNACKS TIME: / / /					
TOTAL					
vs. TARGET					

NOTES

_____

_____

_____

_____

HOW THE DAY WENT? ☐ BAD ☐ OK ☐ GOOD ☐ GREAT

DATE | | ☐☐☐☐☐☐☐ **WEIGHT** **SLEEP** **WATER**
S M T W T F S
POUNDS/KILOS   HOURS   OZ/ml

HOW I FEEL ☺ ☺ ☺ ☹   **ENERGY** ☐⊏⊏⊏⊏⊏▣   **ACTIVITY** 🛏⊏⊏⊏⊏⊏🏃

☐ SUGAR FREE   ☐ ALCOHOL FREE   ☐ GLUTEN FREE   ☐ DAIRY FREE   ☐ LOW CARB   ☐ LOTS OF VEGGIES
☐ ORGANIC   ☐ NO PROCESSED FOODS

BREAKFAST TIME:	SERVING SIZE	PROTEIN	FAT	CARBS	CALORIES
SUBTOTAL					

LUNCH TIME:					
SUBTOTAL					

DINNER TIME:					
SUBTOTAL					

SNACKS TIME: / / /					
TOTAL					
vs. TARGET					

NOTES

_____

_____

_____

_____

HOW THE DAY WENT? ☐ BAD   ☐ OK   ☐ GOOD   ☐ GREAT

DATE | | ☐☐☐☐☐☐☐ **WEIGHT**   **SLEEP**   **WATER**

S M T W T F S

POUNDS/KILOS   HOURS   OZ/ml

HOW I FEEL 😄 🙂 😐 ☹️   **ENERGY** ▯ ⊏▭▭▭⊐ 🔋   **ACTIVITY** 🛏️ ⊏▭▭▭⊐ 🏃

☐ SUGAR FREE   ☐ ALCOHOL FREE   ☐ GLUTEN FREE   ☐ DAIRY FREE   ☐ LOW CARB   ☐ LOTS OF VEGGIES

☐ ORGANIC   ☐ NO PROCESSED FOODS

BREAKFAST TIME:	SERVING SIZE	PROTEIN	FAT	CARBS	CALORIES
SUBTOTAL					
LUNCH TIME:					
SUBTOTAL					
DINNER TIME:					
SUBTOTAL					
SNACKS TIME: / / /					
TOTAL					
vs. TARGET					

NOTES

_____

_____

_____

HOW THE DAY WENT? ☐ BAD ☐ OK ☐ GOOD ☐ GREAT

DATE | | | S M T W T F S | **WEIGHT** POUNDS/KILOS | **SLEEP** HOURS | **WATER** OZ/ml

HOW I FEEL 😄 🙂 😐 ☹️ | **ENERGY** 🔋 ▭▭▭▭▭ 🔋 | **ACTIVITY** 🛏️ ▭▭▭▭ 🏃

| | SUGAR FREE | | ALCOHOL FREE | | GLUTEN FREE | | DAIRY FREE | | LOW CARB | | LOTS OF VEGGIES |
| | ORGANIC | | NO PROCESSED FOODS |

BREAKFAST TIME:	SERVING SIZE	PROTEIN	FAT	CARBS	CALORIES
SUBTOTAL					

LUNCH TIME:					
SUBTOTAL					

DINNER TIME:					
SUBTOTAL					

SNACKS TIME: / / /					
TOTAL					
vs. TARGET					

NOTES

_____

_____

_____

_____

HOW THE DAY WENT? | BAD | OK | GOOD | GREAT |

DATE | | _____ ☐☐☐☐☐☐☐ **WEIGHT** **SLEEP** **WATER**
S M T W T F S ‾‾‾‾‾‾‾‾‾‾‾ ‾‾‾‾‾‾‾‾ ‾‾‾‾‾‾‾
POUNDS/KILOS HOURS OZ/ml

HOW I FEEL 😀 🙂 😐 ☹️   **ENERGY** ▯⊂▭▭▭▭▭▭▭▭▭▭▭▭ 🔋   **ACTIVITY** 🛏⊂▭▭▭▭▭▭▭▭ 🏃

☐ SUGAR FREE   ☐ ALCOHOL FREE   ☐ GLUTEN FREE   ☐ DAIRY FREE   ☐ LOW CARB   ☐ LOTS OF VEGGIES

☐ ORGANIC   ☐ NO PROCESSED FOODS

BREAKFAST TIME:	SERVING SIZE	PROTEIN	FAT	CARBS	CALORIES
SUBTOTAL					

LUNCH TIME:					
SUBTOTAL					

DINNER TIME:					
SUBTOTAL					

SNACKS TIME: / / /					
TOTAL					
vs. TARGET					

NOTES

_____

_____

_____

_____

HOW THE DAY WENT? ☐ BAD ☐ OK ☐ GOOD ☐ GREAT

DATE | | |

S M T W T F S

WEIGHT
POUNDS/KILOS

SLEEP
HOURS

WATER
OZ/ml

HOW I FEEL ☺ ☺ ☺ ☹ **ENERGY** 🔋⊂⊏⊏⊏⊏⊐🔋 **ACTIVITY** 🛏⊂⊏⊏⊏⊏⊐🏃

☐ SUGAR FREE ☐ ALCOHOL FREE ☐ GLUTEN FREE ☐ DAIRY FREE ☐ LOW CARB ☐ LOTS OF VEGGIES
☐ ORGANIC ☐ NO PROCESSED FOODS

BREAKFAST TIME:	SERVING SIZE	PROTEIN	FAT	CARBS	CALORIES
SUBTOTAL					
LUNCH TIME:					
SUBTOTAL					
DINNER TIME:					
SUBTOTAL					
SNACKS TIME: / / /					
TOTAL					
vs. TARGET					

NOTES

_____
_____
_____
_____

HOW THE DAY WENT? ☐ BAD ☐ OK ☐ GOOD ☐ GREAT

DATE | | | ☐☐☐☐☐☐☐ S M T W T F S | **WEIGHT** POUNDS/KILOS | **SLEEP** HOURS | **WATER** OZ/ml

HOW I FEEL 😄 🙂 😐 🙁 **ENERGY** 🔋 ⊏▭▭▭▭▭▭▭⊐ 🔋 **ACTIVITY** 🛏 ⊏▭▭▭▭⊐ 🏃

☐ SUGAR FREE   ☐ ALCOHOL FREE   ☐ GLUTEN FREE   ☐ DAIRY FREE   ☐ LOW CARB   ☐ LOTS OF VEGGIES

☐ ORGANIC   ☐ NO PROCESSED FOODS

BREAKFAST TIME:	SERVING SIZE	PROTEIN	FAT	CARBS	CALORIES
SUBTOTAL					

LUNCH TIME:					
SUBTOTAL					

DINNER TIME:					
SUBTOTAL					

SNACKS TIME: / / /					
TOTAL					
vs. TARGET					

NOTES

_____

_____

_____

_____

HOW THE DAY WENT? ☐ BAD ☐ OK ☐ GOOD ☐ GREAT

DATE | | | □□□□□□□   **WEIGHT**   **SLEEP**   **WATER**

S M T W T F S   POUNDS/KILOS   HOURS   OZ/ml

HOW I FEEL 😄 🙂 😐 ☹️   **ENERGY** 🔋⊏▭▭▭▭⊐🪫   **ACTIVITY** 🛏⊏▭▭▭▭⊐🏃

☐ SUGAR FREE   ☐ ALCOHOL FREE   ☐ GLUTEN FREE   ☐ DAIRY FREE   ☐ LOW CARB   ☐ LOTS OF VEGGIES

☐ ORGANIC   ☐ NO PROCESSED FOODS

BREAKFAST TIME:	SERVING SIZE	PROTEIN	FAT	CARBS	CALORIES
SUBTOTAL					
LUNCH TIME:					
SUBTOTAL					
DINNER TIME:					
SUBTOTAL					
SNACKS TIME: / / /					
TOTAL					
vs. TARGET					

NOTES

_____

_____

_____

_____

HOW THE DAY WENT? ☐ BAD ☐ OK ☐ GOOD ☐ GREAT

DATE | | ☐☐☐☐☐☐☐   **WEIGHT**   **SLEEP**   **WATER**
S M T W T F S   POUNDS/KILOS   HOURS   OZ/ml

HOW I FEEL 😄 🙂 😕 ☹   **ENERGY** 🔋 ⬜⬜⬜⬜ 🔋   **ACTIVITY** 🛏 ⬜⬜⬜ 🏃

☐ SUGAR FREE   ☐ ALCOHOL FREE   ☐ GLUTEN FREE   ☐ DAIRY FREE   ☐ LOW CARB   ☐ LOTS OF VEGGIES
☐ ORGANIC   ☐ NO PROCESSED FOODS

BREAKFAST TIME:	SERVING SIZE	PROTEIN	FAT	CARBS	CALORIES
SUBTOTAL					
LUNCH TIME:					
SUBTOTAL					
DINNER TIME:					
SUBTOTAL					
SNACKS TIME: / / /					
TOTAL					
vs. TARGET					

NOTES

_____
_____
_____
_____

HOW THE DAY WENT? ☐ BAD   ☐ OK   ☐ GOOD   ☐ GREAT

DATE | |

S M T W T F S

WEIGHT _____
POUNDS/KILOS

SLEEP _____
HOURS

WATER _____
OZ/ml

HOW I FEEL 😄 🙂 😐 ☹️   ENERGY 🔋 ⊂▭▭▭▭⊃ 🔋   ACTIVITY 🛏️ ⊂▭▭▭⊃ 🏃

☐ SUGAR FREE ☐ ALCOHOL FREE ☐ GLUTEN FREE ☐ DAIRY FREE ☐ LOW CARB ☐ LOTS OF VEGGIES
☐ ORGANIC ☐ NO PROCESSED FOODS

BREAKFAST TIME:	SERVING SIZE	PROTEIN	FAT	CARBS	CALORIES
SUBTOTAL					
LUNCH TIME:					
SUBTOTAL					
DINNER TIME:					
SUBTOTAL					
SNACKS TIME: / / /					
TOTAL					
vs. TARGET					

NOTES
_____
_____
_____
_____

HOW THE DAY WENT? ☐ BAD ☐ OK ☐ GOOD ☐ GREAT

DATE | | | ☐☐☐☐☐☐☐ | **WEIGHT** | **SLEEP** | **WATER**
S M T W T F S | POUNDS/KILOS | HOURS | OZ/ml

HOW I FEEL 😄 ☺ 😐 ☹ **ENERGY** 🔋 ⊏☐☐☐☐⊐ 🔋 **ACTIVITY** 🛏 ⊏☐☐☐☐⊐ 🏃

☐ SUGAR FREE ☐ ALCOHOL FREE ☐ GLUTEN FREE ☐ DAIRY FREE ☐ LOW CARB ☐ LOTS OF VEGGIES
☐ ORGANIC ☐ NO PROCESSED FOODS

BREAKFAST TIME:	SERVING SIZE	PROTEIN	FAT	CARBS	CALORIES
SUBTOTAL					
LUNCH TIME:					
SUBTOTAL					
DINNER TIME:					
SUBTOTAL					
SNACKS TIME: / / /					
TOTAL					
vs. TARGET					

NOTES

_____
_____
_____
_____

HOW THE DAY WENT? ☐ BAD ☐ OK ☐ GOOD ☐ GREAT

DATE | |

S M T W T F S

WEIGHT
POUNDS/KILOS

SLEEP
HOURS

WATER
OZ/ml

HOW I FEEL 😄 ☺ 😐 ☹   ENERGY 🔋⊏▭▭▭▭⊐🔋   ACTIVITY 🛏⊏▭▭▭▭⊐🏃

| | SUGAR FREE | | ALCOHOL FREE | | GLUTEN FREE | | DAIRY FREE | | LOW CARB | | LOTS OF VEGGIES |
| | ORGANIC | | NO PROCESSED FOODS |

BREAKFAST TIME:	SERVING SIZE	PROTEIN	FAT	CARBS	CALORIES
SUBTOTAL					

LUNCH TIME:					
SUBTOTAL					

DINNER TIME:					
SUBTOTAL					

SNACKS TIME: / / /					
TOTAL					
vs. TARGET					

NOTES

_____

_____

_____

_____

HOW THE DAY WENT? [BAD] [OK] [GOOD] [GREAT]

DATE | |

S M T W T F S

WEIGHT
POUNDS/KILOS

SLEEP
HOURS

WATER
OZ/ml

HOW I FEEL 😄 🙂 😐 ☹️   **ENERGY** 🔋 ⎯⎯⎯ 🔋   **ACTIVITY** 🛏️ ⎯⎯⎯ 🏃

☐ SUGAR FREE ☐ ALCOHOL FREE ☐ GLUTEN FREE ☐ DAIRY FREE ☐ LOW CARB ☐ LOTS OF VEGGIES
☐ ORGANIC ☐ NO PROCESSED FOODS

BREAKFAST TIME:	SERVING SIZE	PROTEIN	FAT	CARBS	CALORIES
SUBTOTAL					
LUNCH TIME:					
SUBTOTAL					
DINNER TIME:					
SUBTOTAL					
SNACKS TIME: / / /					
TOTAL					
vs. TARGET					

NOTES

_____

_____

_____

_____

HOW THE DAY WENT? | BAD | OK | GOOD | GREAT |

DATE | |

| S | M | T | W | T | F | S |

WEIGHT
POUNDS/KILOS

SLEEP
HOURS

WATER
OZ/ml

HOW I FEEL 😄 🙂 😐 ☹️   ENERGY 🔋 ⊂▭▭▭▭⊃ 🔋   ACTIVITY 🛏️ ⊂▭▭▭▭⊃ 🏃

☐ SUGAR FREE   ☐ ALCOHOL FREE   ☐ GLUTEN FREE   ☐ DAIRY FREE   ☐ LOW CARB   ☐ LOTS OF VEGGIES
☐ ORGANIC   ☐ NO PROCESSED FOODS

BREAKFAST TIME:	SERVING SIZE	PROTEIN	FAT	CARBS	CALORIES
SUBTOTAL					

LUNCH TIME:					
SUBTOTAL					

DINNER TIME:					
SUBTOTAL					

SNACKS TIME: / / /					
TOTAL					
vs. TARGET					

NOTES
_____
_____
_____
_____

HOW THE DAY WENT? ☐ BAD ☐ OK ☐ GOOD ☐ GREAT

DATE | | ☐☐☐☐☐☐☐   **WEIGHT**   **SLEEP**   **WATER**
S   M   T   W   T   F   S   POUNDS/KILOS   HOURS   OZ/ml

HOW I FEEL ☺ ☺ ☺ ☹   **ENERGY** ▯⊂▭▭▭▭▭▯   **ACTIVITY** ⊨⊂▭▭▭▭▯ 🏃

☐ SUGAR FREE   ☐ ALCOHOL FREE   ☐ GLUTEN FREE   ☐ DAIRY FREE   ☐ LOW CARB   ☐ LOTS OF VEGGIES

☐ ORGANIC   ☐ NO PROCESSED FOODS

BREAKFAST TIME:	SERVING SIZE	PROTEIN	FAT	CARBS	CALORIES
SUBTOTAL					

LUNCH TIME:					
SUBTOTAL					

DINNER TIME:					
SUBTOTAL					

SNACKS TIME: / / /					
TOTAL					
vs. TARGET					

NOTES

_____

_____

_____

_____

HOW THE DAY WENT? | BAD | OK | GOOD | GREAT |

DATE | | ☐☐☐☐☐☐☐ **WEIGHT** **SLEEP** **WATER**
S M T W T F S   POUNDS/KILOS   HOURS   OZ/ml

HOW I FEEL 😄 🙂 😐 🙁   ENERGY 🔋 ⊏▭▭▭▭⊐ 🔋   ACTIVITY 🛏 ⊏▭▭▭⊐ 🏃

☐ SUGAR FREE   ☐ ALCOHOL FREE   ☐ GLUTEN FREE   ☐ DAIRY FREE   ☐ LOW CARB   ☐ LOTS OF VEGGIES
☐ ORGANIC   ☐ NO PROCESSED FOODS

BREAKFAST TIME:	SERVING SIZE	PROTEIN	FAT	CARBS	CALORIES
SUBTOTAL					
LUNCH TIME:					
SUBTOTAL					
DINNER TIME:					
SUBTOTAL					
SNACKS TIME: / / /					
TOTAL					
vs. TARGET					

NOTES

HOW THE DAY WENT? ☐ BAD   ☐ OK   ☐ GOOD   ☐ GREAT

DATE | | ☐☐☐☐☐☐☐   **WEIGHT**   **SLEEP**   **WATER**

S M T W T F S   POUNDS/KILOS   HOURS   OZ/ml

HOW I FEEL 😄 🙂 😐 🙁   **ENERGY** ▯━━━━━▮   **ACTIVITY** 🛏━━━━━ 🏃

☐ SUGAR FREE   ☐ ALCOHOL FREE   ☐ GLUTEN FREE   ☐ DAIRY FREE   ☐ LOW CARB   ☐ LOTS OF VEGGIES

☐ ORGANIC   ☐ NO PROCESSED FOODS

BREAKFAST TIME:	SERVING SIZE	PROTEIN	FAT	CARBS	CALORIES
SUBTOTAL					
LUNCH TIME:					
SUBTOTAL					
DINNER TIME:					
SUBTOTAL					
SNACKS TIME: / / /					
TOTAL					
vs. TARGET					

NOTES

_____

_____

_____

HOW THE DAY WENT? ☐ BAD ☐ OK ☐ GOOD ☐ GREAT

DATE | | | S M T W T F S **WEIGHT** POUNDS/KILOS **SLEEP** HOURS **WATER** OZ/ml

HOW I FEEL ☺ ☺ ☹ ☹   ENERGY ▯ ⊂▭▭▭▭⊃ ▮   ACTIVITY 🛏 ⊂▭▭▭⊃ 🏃

☐ SUGAR FREE   ☐ ALCOHOL FREE   ☐ GLUTEN FREE   ☐ DAIRY FREE   ☐ LOW CARB   ☐ LOTS OF VEGGIES
☐ ORGANIC   ☐ NO PROCESSED FOODS

BREAKFAST TIME:	SERVING SIZE	PROTEIN	FAT	CARBS	CALORIES
SUBTOTAL					
LUNCH TIME:					
SUBTOTAL					
DINNER TIME:					
SUBTOTAL					
SNACKS TIME: / / /					
TOTAL					
vs. TARGET					

NOTES
_____
_____
_____
_____

HOW THE DAY WENT? ☐ BAD ☐ OK ☐ GOOD ☐ GREAT

DATE | |

WEIGHT
S M T W T F S
POUNDS/KILOS

SLEEP
HOURS

WATER
OZ/ml

HOW I FEEL 😄 🙂 😐 ☹️   ENERGY ▯⊏▭▭▭▭⊐🔋   ACTIVITY 🛏⊏▭▭▭▭⊐🏃

☐ SUGAR FREE ☐ ALCOHOL FREE ☐ GLUTEN FREE ☐ DAIRY FREE ☐ LOW CARB ☐ LOTS OF VEGGIES

☐ ORGANIC ☐ NO PROCESSED FOODS

BREAKFAST TIME:	SERVING SIZE	PROTEIN	FAT	CARBS	CALORIES
SUBTOTAL					
LUNCH TIME:					
SUBTOTAL					
DINNER TIME:					
SUBTOTAL					
SNACKS TIME: / / /					
TOTAL					
vs. TARGET					

NOTES

_____

_____

_____

_____

HOW THE DAY WENT? ☐ BAD ☐ OK ☐ GOOD ☐ GREAT

DATE | |

S M T W T F S

WEIGHT — POUNDS/KILOS

SLEEP — HOURS

WATER — OZ/ml

HOW I FEEL ☺ ☺ ☺ ☹   **ENERGY** 🔋⊏▭▭▭⊐🔋   **ACTIVITY** 🛏⊏▭▭▭⊐🏃

| | SUGAR FREE | | ALCOHOL FREE | | GLUTEN FREE | | DAIRY FREE | | LOW CARB | | LOTS OF VEGGIES |
| | ORGANIC | | NO PROCESSED FOODS |

BREAKFAST TIME:	SERVING SIZE	PROTEIN	FAT	CARBS	CALORIES
SUBTOTAL					
LUNCH TIME:					
SUBTOTAL					
DINNER TIME:					
SUBTOTAL					
SNACKS TIME: / / /					
TOTAL					
vs. TARGET					

NOTES
_____
_____
_____
_____

HOW THE DAY WENT? | BAD | OK | GOOD | GREAT |

DATE | | | ☐☐☐☐☐☐☐ **WEIGHT** **SLEEP** **WATER**
S M T W T F S

POUNDS/KILOS HOURS OZ/ml

HOW I FEEL 😀 🙂 😐 ☹️ **ENERGY** ▯⊂▭▭▭▭▭▭▯ **ACTIVITY** 🛏⊂▭▭▭▭▭▭ 🏃

☐ SUGAR FREE ☐ ALCOHOL FREE ☐ GLUTEN FREE ☐ DAIRY FREE ☐ LOW CARB ☐ LOTS OF VEGGIES
☐ ORGANIC ☐ NO PROCESSED FOODS

BREAKFAST TIME:	SERVING SIZE	PROTEIN	FAT	CARBS	CALORIES
SUBTOTAL					
LUNCH TIME:					
SUBTOTAL					
DINNER TIME:					
SUBTOTAL					
SNACKS TIME: / / /					
TOTAL					
vs. TARGET					

NOTES

_____

_____

_____

_____

HOW THE DAY WENT? ☐ BAD ☐ OK ☐ GOOD ☐ GREAT

DATE | | SMTWTFS □□□□□□□

WEIGHT _____ POUNDS/KILOS

SLEEP _____ HOURS

WATER _____ OZ/ml

HOW I FEEL ☺ ☺ ☺ ☹   **ENERGY** 🔋 ⊂▭▭▭▭ 🔋   **ACTIVITY** 🛏 ⊂▭▭▭ 🏃

☐ SUGAR FREE   ☐ ALCOHOL FREE   ☐ GLUTEN FREE   ☐ DAIRY FREE   ☐ LOW CARB   ☐ LOTS OF VEGGIES
☐ ORGANIC   ☐ NO PROCESSED FOODS

BREAKFAST TIME:	SERVING SIZE	PROTEIN	FAT	CARBS	CALORIES
SUBTOTAL					

LUNCH TIME:					
SUBTOTAL					

DINNER TIME:					
SUBTOTAL					

SNACKS TIME: / / /					
TOTAL					
vs. TARGET					

NOTES

_____
_____
_____
_____

HOW THE DAY WENT? ☐ BAD ☐ OK ☐ GOOD ☐ GREAT

DATE | | ☐☐☐☐☐☐☐ **WEIGHT** **SLEEP** **WATER**
       S M T W T F S   POUNDS/KILOS   HOURS   OZ/ml

HOW I FEEL 😀 🙂 😐 ☹️   **ENERGY** 🔋⊏⊐⊐⊐⊏🔋   **ACTIVITY** 🛏️⊏⊐⊐⊐⊏ 🏃

☐ SUGAR FREE   ☐ ALCOHOL FREE   ☐ GLUTEN FREE   ☐ DAIRY FREE   ☐ LOW CARB   ☐ LOTS OF VEGGIES
☐ ORGANIC   ☐ NO PROCESSED FOODS

BREAKFAST TIME:	SERVING SIZE	PROTEIN	FAT	CARBS	CALORIES
SUBTOTAL					
LUNCH TIME:					
SUBTOTAL					
DINNER TIME:					
SUBTOTAL					
SNACKS TIME: / / /					
TOTAL					
vs. TARGET					

NOTES

_____

_____

_____

_____

HOW THE DAY WENT? ☐ BAD ☐ OK ☐ GOOD ☐ GREAT

DATE | |

S M T W T F S

WEIGHT
POUNDS/KILOS

SLEEP
HOURS

WATER
OZ/ml

HOW I FEEL 😀 🙂 😐 🙁   **ENERGY** 🔋⊂▭▭▭▭⊃🔋   **ACTIVITY** 🛏⊂▭▭▭▭⊃🏃

☐ SUGAR FREE   ☐ ALCOHOL FREE   ☐ GLUTEN FREE   ☐ DAIRY FREE   ☐ LOW CARB   ☐ LOTS OF VEGGIES

☐ ORGANIC   ☐ NO PROCESSED FOODS

BREAKFAST TIME:	SERVING SIZE	PROTEIN	FAT	CARBS	CALORIES
SUBTOTAL					

LUNCH TIME:					
SUBTOTAL					

DINNER TIME:					
SUBTOTAL					

SNACKS TIME: / / /					
TOTAL					
vs. TARGET					

NOTES

_____

_____

_____

_____

HOW THE DAY WENT? ☐ BAD   ☐ OK   ☐ GOOD   ☐ GREAT

NOTES